◆FOCUS◆
Reading for Success

Up and Over

PROGRAM AUTHORS
Richard L. Allington
Ronald L. Cramer
Patricia M. Cunningham
G. Yvonne Pérez
Constance Frazier Robinson
Robert J. Tierney

PROGRAM CONSULTANTS
Bernadine J. Bolden
Ann Hall
Sylvia M. Lee
Dolores Perez
Jo Ann Wong

CRITIC READERS
Sandy Anderson
John Rabets
Jane Thomaston

John C. Manning, *Instructional Consultant*

SCOTT, FORESMAN AND COMPANY
Editorial Offices: Glenview, Illinois

Regional Sales Offices: Palo Alto, California •
Tucker, Georgia • Glenview, Illinois •
Oakland, New Jersey • Dallas, Texas

ACKNOWLEDGMENTS

Text

A Dinosaur Is Too Big (text only) by Elizabeth Bram. Copyright © 1977 by Elizabeth Bram. Adapted by permission of Greenwillow Books (A Division of William Morrow & Company).

Jim Meets The Thing by Miriam Cohen. Copyright © 1981 by Miriam Cohen. Adapted by permission of Greenwillow Books (A Division of William Morrow & Company).

Adapted from *The Oldest Kid*, text © 1981 by Elaine Knox-Wagner. Reprinted with the permission of Albert Whitman & Company.

From "You Do It Too" by Margaret Langford from *Child Education*. Reprinted by permission of Bell & Hyman Limited.

From "The King's Balloon" by D. L. Halterman. Copyright © 1982 by Unity School of Christianity. Reprinted by permission of the author.

From *Taffy and Melissa Molasses* by Carolyn Haywood, Copyright © 1969 by Carolyn Haywood. Adapted by permission of William Morrow & Company.

Adaptation of *One Tough Turkey* by Steven Kroll. Copyright © 1982 by Steven Kroll. Reprinted by permission of Holiday House, Inc. and Joan Daves.

Photographs

Page 96: (top) Steve Smith/Gamma-Liaison; Page 96: (bottom) Kaku Kurita/Gamma-Liaison; Page 97: P. Tatiner/Gamma-Liaison; Page 103, 104 (top/bottom), 105: Gentle Jungle, Inc.; Page 109: Al Kaufman/BOYS' LIFE; Page 170–171: Craig Aurness/West Light; Page 174: Chuck Place; Page 175: Craig Aurness/West Light; Page 176: Chuck Place; Page 177: Vicki Joyce/Hillstrom Stock Photo; Page 179: Joanne M. Benes CTC; Page 194: "George Washington" by Gilbert Stuart, 1795. The Metropolitan Museum of Art, Rogers Fund, 1907; Page 196: Scott, Foresman; Page 217: Grandma Moses, July Fourth. Copyright 1979, Grandma Moses Properties Co., New York, In the White House Collection.

Artists

Adams, Angela 61; Allen, Dave 46; Anderson Bill and Judie 102–108; Beckes, Shirley 116, 227; Bernal, Richard 218–226; Bornholt, Karen Jean 158–159; Cody, Brian 156; Craig, John 172, 204–205; Day, Betsy 50–51, 74–75, 132–133; Eberbach, Andrea 16–20; Frederick, Larry 197; Frazee, Marla 130–131; Fuh-Lin-Hsin 41–44; Geyer, Jackie 12–13, 26; Gustafson, Scott 162–168; Hahn, Marika 208–209; Halverson, Lydia 11, 52–57, 59; Higgins, Pamela 134–138; Iosa, Ann 146–147; Lazarevich, Mila 155–158; Leonard, Tom 142–143; Lexa, Susan 210–216; Lidbeck, Karen 38–39; McCue, Lisa 22–23; Miyake, Yoshi 76–82, 181, 140–141; Miyamoto, Linda 35; Munger, Nancy 84–85; Neill, Eileen Mueller 157; Palmer, Jan 193; Peterson, Bill 144; Pritzen, Barbara 100–101; Rigie, Jane 117; Robinson, James 160–161; Roth, Gail, 118–119, 198–203; Rutherford, Jenny 14–15, 120–121; Scott, Jerry 24, 72–73, 206; Signorino, Slug 66–70; Smith Raymond 83; Snyder, Joel 122–128; Springer, Sally 88–93; Tenz, Freya 110–114; Tiritilli, Jerry 192; Wallner, Alexandra 48–49; Wilson, Ann 152–154; Wimmer, Chuck 48

Freelance Photographs

Ryan Roessler 64–65; Jim Whitmer Photography 4, 28–33, 36–37, 62–63

Contents

Section One

Pick a Pet

What is the right size for a pet?   12–21
What happens when a pet gets lost?   22–35
What can we learn from a pet?   36–46

Walking the Dog

Is the boy walking the dog, or is the dog walking the boy? The dog looks happy, but the boy does not look very happy.

If you could have a pet, what kind of pet would you like to take home? What size pet do you think would be happy in your home?

Places for Silky and Goldie

Silky is a big dog. Silky was Josie's pet. For a while, she lived in Josie's small apartment. Silky was not happy there because the apartment was too small for her.

If Silky wagged her tail, she would knock something over. If she barked, the neighbors complained. But there was something else not good at all. Silky could not exercise. There was no room in the apartment for her to exercise.

Silky went to live with some new people. They lived on a farm. Anyone can guess how happy she was. She could wag her tail. She could bark loudly. And no one complained. Best of all, Silky could run far and wide.

But Josie was not happy. She wanted a pet. So she got a goldfish to live with her in the apartment. She put the goldfish in a tank.

For a goldfish, Goldie was very big. But goldfish are not too big anyway. Goldie could wag his tail all he wanted. He got all the exercise he needed in his tank. And Goldie did not bark loudly enough for anyone in the apartment to complain about.

Silky and Goldie and Josie were happy.

Sharpen Your Skills

Think about if Silky, Goldie, and Josie all got what they needed. This will help you know what the story is all about.

1. Who is the story about?
2. What is the story all about?
   a. Silky needed more room and went to a farm. Then Josie got a goldfish instead.
   b. Josie lives in an apartment.

As you read the story, "A Dinosaur Is Too Big," think of what the story is all about.

15

A Dinosaur Is Too Big

by Elizabeth Bram

My mother said I could have an animal all my own. So I think it would be fun to have a fox. But a fox is not really big enough. Maybe I should get a pig.

Anyway a pig is not really big enough either. Maybe I should get a big fish.

I could go down to the river and put it in a tank. I could carry it home in my wagon.

But really, I need something bigger than a fish. Maybe a horse . . . or a camel! Anyway, I could go to the desert and get a camel. Then I could use my sandbox. I could put the camel in my sandbox. The camel would feel at home in my sandbox.

A camel is bigger than a fox. It is bigger than a pig. It is bigger than a fish. And it is bigger than a horse. But it is not really big enough. I want something BIG.

An elephant! I could put an elephant in my yard. But an elephant is not big enough. I want something BIG. Maybe what I really need is. . .

A DINOSAUR!

A dinosaur is big enough. You can climb up his back and pick apples from a tree. Then you can slide down his back. You can talk with anyone at his or her apartment windows.

But . . . a dinosaur is so big that you would need a ladder to climb up on him. Climbing is a lot of work. He would take up the whole yard. So I guess there would be no room to play in the yard. A dinosaur is very tall. So you would have to call very loudly when you called him. He could not sleep on your bed. You would have to use a lot of time bringing him food. Dinosaurs eat a lot.

I guess a dinosaur is too big. A fox is too big. A pig is too big. A horse is too big. A camel is too big. And an elephant is too big too. I really need an animal more my own size, something small . . . like ME.

Checking Comprehension and Skills

1. What size pet did the girl in the story want at first? (17)
2. Why would a dinosaur make a good pet? (19)
3. What size pet did the girl get? (21)
4. Do you think the girl picked the right pet? Why or why not?
●5. What is this story all about?
   a. A camel would feel at home in a sandbox.
   b. At first, the girl wanted a big pet, but, then she wanted a small one.

   Which word is best in the blank?
○6. Dinosaurs eat a l_t of food.
    late   lot   ton

   ● Story Elements: Main idea
   ○ Context and consonants

Puppies

These puppies are sisters and brothers. No two puppies are quite the same. The puppies may not be the same, but they all have the same needs. Soon the puppies will be old enough to go to new homes. They will still need people to take care of them.

Using Sense and Consonants

My dog and I had fun in the **p_rk.**

What word goes at the end of the sentence above? Can you think of a word that makes sense? Try one of these words:

pack   park   zoo

Sharpen Your Skills

Both park and zoo make sense in the sentence. But only park has the same consonants as **p_rk.**

When you come to a word you don't know, think of a word that makes sense in the sentence. Then see if the consonants in your word are the same as the consonants in the new word.

What words go in these sentences?
1. Don't br_ng your dog to school with you.
   bring   take   brick
2. My sm_ll dog is more fun than a big dog.
   smell   little   small

Did you pick <u>bring</u> and <u>small</u>? Now read the words in these sentences.
3. My kitten <u>slept</u> on my bed with me.
4. I <u>toss</u> the ball and my dog goes after it.
5. The dog always comes when I <u>yell</u> for her.

Use sense and consonants to help you read new words as you read more about pets.

Let the Tag Do the Talking

Do you have a pet? You have to take good care of a pet. You have to feed it. You have to make sure it gets exercise. You have to keep it clean too. You should also have an ID tag for your pet.

Every dog and cat should have an ID tag. Sometimes dogs and cats get lost. But a dog or cat could not say where it lives. An ID tag can talk for a pet. Look at the dog in the picture. It could not tell you its name. But its ID tag does.

An ID tag tells a lot about your pet. It gives the animal's name. It gives the street name and number where the owner lives. It also gives the city and state. It may give the owner's telephone number.

Has your pet ever been lost? Then you know how good it feels to get a telephone call at night. The telephone call tells you your dog was found. The tag did the talking.

Sharpen Your Skills

This article is all about ID tags for pets. Each group of sentences tells about ID tags. Look at the last group of sentences on page 26.

1. Which sentence tells you the most important idea about ID tags?
2. Why should pets have ID tags?

As you read "Taking Care of Your Dog," think of what the story is all about.

Taking Care of Your Dog

by Suzanne Massey

Dogs are wet noses. Dogs are kisses. The kisses are wet kisses. Dogs are friends. Dogs are fun. Dogs need people as friends. People take care of dogs.

Donald, Maria, Jason, and Kyoko own dogs. The children take care of their own dogs. The children give them food. They give them water. And, they give them exercise.

All dogs need food. Donald's dog is named Pal. Pal is a big, friendly dog who likes to eat. He would like to eat ten meals a day. Donald feeds him only one meal a day. Donald knows that too much food could make Pal fat or sick.

Maria's dog is named Cupcake. Cupcake is only a puppy. Maria feeds her about three meals a day. A puppy must eat more times a day than an older dog.

Dogs need other things. They need water. A dog should have a pan of water. The water should be clean. Maria gives Cupcake clean water five times a day. Cupcake is a little messy. She likes to stand in her water pan. Maria puts newspapers under the pan to catch the water.

Just like children, dogs need exercise. Small dogs need less exercise than big dogs. Jason has a small dog. Her name is Hildy. Jason and Hildy live in an apartment. On nice days they take walks in the park. Jason keeps Hildy on a leash. On wet days they play in the apartment. Hildy gets other exercise by running around the apartment.

Kyoko's dog is named Wolf. Wolf is a big dog. Wolf needs lots of exercise. Kyoko lives in a house with a big yard. Wolf exercises in the yard. He plays ball with Kyoko. Kyoko throws the ball around the yard. Wolf brings it back. Kyoko keeps Wolf running around the yard. Running makes Wolf feel good.

Dogs need food and exercise. They also need other things. They need a clean place to sleep. They need a brush for their hair. They need baths. Dogs even need to go to the doctor.

Dogs need a place to sleep. Maria made a good bed for Cupcake. She made it out of wood. She put torn newspapers in the bed. The newspapers made the bed soft. Maria also put a clock in the bed. The clock made a loud sound. Cupcake is just a puppy. Sometimes she feels lost at night. But the sound of the clock makes Cupcake happy at night. Cupcake thinks the sound of the clock is her mother by her side. Then Cupcake is not afraid at night.

Donald has a brush for Pal. He uses the brush on Pal's hair every day. This makes Pal feel good. It also keeps him clean.

Sometimes Pal likes to roll in the mud. Then Donald gives him a bath. He puts water in a tub. The water is not too hot or too cold. Pal likes to have baths. He also likes to shake the water off after his bath. This is when Donald gets very wet!

Veterinarians are animal doctors. Dogs have to go to the doctor just like people. Veterinarians can let you know a lot about your dog. Veterinarians can help you care for your dog.

The children love their dogs. They play with them. They take good care of them.

Checking Comprehension and Skills

•1. This story is about how dog owners must make sure their dogs get what they need. Look at the last group of sentences on page 29. Which sentence there tells the most important idea about what dogs need?

2. Do you think Pal would be happy living in Jason's apartment? Why or why not? (29, 31)

3. Do you think the dogs in this story feel loved? Why or why not? (34)

Which word is best in the blank?
○4. Small dogs need l_ss exercise.
more   less   lose
○5. Sometimes Pal likes to r_ll in the mud.
really   play   roll

• Main idea and supporting details
○ Context and consonants

Your Dog's Toy Box

Find a shoe box. Then find pictures of dogs and cut them out. Paste the pictures on the box. Write your dog's name on the box.

Put your dog's toys in the box. Give it to your dog on its birthday. If you don't have a dog, you could give it to a friend's dog.

The Classroom Pet

The children in the picture are learning about a classroom pet while they feed it. They are looking at the pet through a glass. The glass makes the pet look bigger. They see how the pet moves its mouth when it eats.

Hopper and Happy

"Look at Happy go on the wheel!" said Jeff.

"Maybe Happy runs so fast because he needs a lot of exercise," Trina said.

"What about Hopper?" asked Jeff. "Hopper can't get any exercise because Happy always uses the wheel."

"Hopper can use the wheel now," said Debby. "Happy is getting off the wheel because he is tired."

Jeff laughed, "Happy is not the only one who needs rest. Hopper got tired watching Happy run. He got tired so he went to sleep."

The children went to lunch. When they came back to the classroom, Debby said, "Hopper is missing."

"The cage door is open," said Trina.

Jeff said, "Hopper and Happy's water splashed out of the pan. So I went to fill it. I guess I left the door open."

"He can't be too far away," said Debby.

Everybody looked in the classroom. Then they saw Hopper. He climbed the table leg and went back into his cage.

Trina laughed, "Hopper found another way to exercise because Happy always uses the wheel."

Sharpen Your Skills

A story tells you things that happen. The words <u>so</u> and <u>because</u> tell you why they happen.
1. Why did Hopper find another way to exercise?
2. Why did Jeff fill Hopper and Happy's pan?

Find out why an ant farm is a lot of work in the next story, "Weekend Ants."

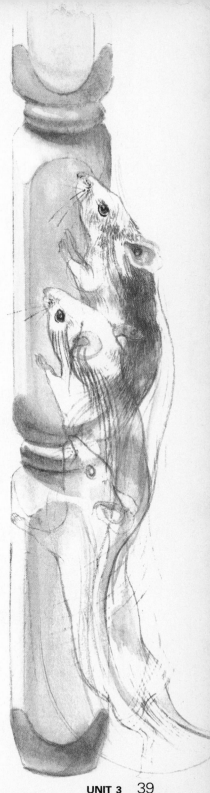

Weekend Ants

by Martha Weintraub

All the children loved the ant farm in their classroom. Each Friday one girl or boy got to take the ant farm home for the weekend.

Mark was very happy because this Friday it was his turn. He loved looking at the ants. There were many other things to do in the classroom. This Friday night he could watch the ants as much as he wanted.

"Mom! Mom!" Mark called, "I have the ant farm! I get to keep it for the weekend!"

"Oh, that is wonderful!" said Mark's mother. "Where are you going to keep it?"

"On the table by my bed, I guess. It does not take up much room, and there is no mess at all. I just have to give the ants food and water," said Mark.

Mark's little brother Charley came in. His brother hated ants and bugs. So when he saw the ant farm, he screamed.

"Oh, Charley. It's all right," said Mom. "The ants can't get out."

"Well, as long as they can't get out. I guess it's all right," said Charley.

"Charley," said Mark. "Look here. The ants are really fun to watch. These little ants are the workers. This big one is the queen."

"I guess they are not too bad," his brother said. "As long as they can't get out of the farm, that is."

"They can't," said Mark.

That night Mark put the ant farm on the table by his bed so he could watch it until he went to sleep.

The next morning, Mark stretched and stretched as he woke up. As he stretched, he knocked the ant farm off the table. It split open. Sand spilled out. The ants started to get out. They spread here. They spread there. They spread out all over.

Just then Charley came in. "Bugs!" he screamed. "Bugs! Bugs are all over the room!" He screamed and screamed.

Mark yelled, "Stop it, Charley! Stop!"

Rags, the dog, came in because of Charley's screaming. Rags started to run all over the room.

"Mom," yelled Mark. "Help! I broke the ant farm. Get Rags and Charley out of here!"

Mark's mother was coming up the steps with clean clothes. Just then one of the ants bit Rags. Rags ran down the steps. He knocked the clothes out of Mom's hands. Some clothes went with him. Rags ran into the plant stand because he could not see where he was going. So the plant stand fell and broke.

Mom left the mess and went to Mark's room. Mark was trying to put sand and ants into a jar. "I have got to find the queen, Mom. These other ants need the queen," Mark yelled. "She is the mother to all of the ants."

"I'll help," said Mom. "Charley, you can be a big help too. Pick up the clothes on the steps, and keep away from the plant mess. Thank you, Charley."

Mom and Mark looked and looked, but they could not find the queen. Then Mom looked in part of the ant farm that still had some sand in it.

"Is this the queen?" she asked.

"Yes!" said Mark. "Oh, Mom! Thank you!"

"Good," said Mom. "Now you can help me clean up the other mess."

While Mark and his mother were cleaning up the plant mess, she started to laugh. "Ant farms are easy to take care of," she said. "No mess at all."

Mark had to laugh too.

Checking Comprehension and Skills

●1. Why was Mark happy at the beginning of the story? (40)

●2. Why did Mark say the ant farm would be no mess at all? (40)

3. What happened to the ant farm? (42)

4. How did Mark feel when his mom found the queen ant? (44)

5. Would you like an ant farm? Why or why not?

Which word is best in the blank?

○6. The ant farm spl_t open when it fell.

broke   split   spot

○7. The ant farm broke, and s_nd spilled out.

dirt   send   sand

● Cause and effect relationships   ○ Context and consonants

What's in the Book?

Looking for something? Let's say you want to find one story in a book. Do you have to go through all the <u>pages</u> until you find it? No. You can use the Table of Contents.

The Table of Contents is a list that tells what is in the book. Here is how to use it.

1. Look for it at the beginning of the book.
2. Then look down the list of story names until you find the one you want.
3. Look at the number. It tells you the page where the story begins.

Find the Table of Contents at the beginning of this book. Now look up the story "Taking Care of Your Dog." On what page does it begin? Now try to find the story in this book.

To find a story, use the Table of Contents. It's always in the beginning of the book.

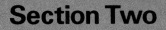

Showtime

47

The Show Begins

People are still coming in. Many are seated. Everybody is talking and laughing. Soon the lights go out. No one makes another sound. The curtain goes up. The play is about to begin.

Curtain Going Up

"It's almost curtain time," said the teacher. "Is everybody ready?"

It was the night of the class play. They were putting on <u>Red</u> <u>Ridinghood</u>.

Karen had on a long red cape. "Harry," she said. "Is my cape all right?"

"Yes," said Harry.

Karen picked up her basket. It was the basket she took to Grandma's house in the play. The basket shouldn't have had a thing in it. But it felt as if it did. She opened the top.

She jumped! An awful face looked up at her! It had a long nose, big eyes, and fur!

"Is something in your basket?" Harry asked.

"Very funny, Harry." Karen handed him the face. It was his mask for the play.

"Is my costume zipped up?" he asked. Harry's costume zipped up the back. It had a long fur tail.

"I'll zip it for you," said Karen.

"Thanks. Your red cape is nice," Harry said. "But my costume is great. I have a mask over my face. No one will know it's me."

"Yes they will," said Karen. "They will know it must be you. You play just as many tricks in the play as you really do every day."

Sharpen Your Skills

When you read, sometimes you have to figure out things on your own. You can figure out what is not said by thinking about the details in the story.

1. Karen will be Red Ridinghood in the play. What details help you know this is true?
2. Harry likes to play tricks on people. What details in the story tell you that?

As you read the next play, try to figure out how the shoemaker and his wife feel about the elves.

The Elves and the Shoemaker

Made into a play
by Sharon Fear

CAST
The Storyteller
The Shoemaker
The Shoemaker's Wife
Two Elves
Man Shopper
Woman Shopper

Act 1

STORYTELLER: Once there was a shoemaker.
He and his wife were good people.
They worked very hard. But hard as
they worked, they could not seem to
make a living. (*The curtain rises. The
shoemaker is working in his shop. His wife
comes in.*)

WIFE: You should go to bed. It's late.

SHOEMAKER: I am cutting out leather for a pair of shoes. This is all the leather we have left. It's just enough for one pair of shoes.

WIFE: Try not to think about it. Come and rest. We can make the shoes in the morning. *(They go out. The shop gets dark.)*

STORYTELLER: So they went to bed. Deep in sleep, they could not know that something was happening in the shop. *(Two elves come in. They make a pair of shoes. Then they depart.)* But in the morning as the sun rises. . . . *(The shop gets light. The shoemaker and his wife come in.)*

SHOEMAKER: Look! A pair of shoes! Now where do you suppose they came from? *(a knock at the door)* Somebody is knocking. I'll see who it is. Let us hope it is somebody needing shoes! *(He goes to the door.)*

WIFE: Let us hope so indeed! Those shoes are very fine shoes. I wonder where they came from. *(The shoemaker opens the door.)*

MAN *(He comes in and looks at the shoes.)*: What fine shoes! I would like to buy them. *(He pays the shoemaker.)*

SHOEMAKER: Thank you! *(He opens the door. The man departs.)* He gave me quite a lot for them. It's enough to buy more leather. The new leather will make two pairs of shoes!

STORYTELLER: So the shoemaker and his wife got more leather. They cut the leather for two pairs of shoes. *(The shoemaker and his wife are cutting leather.)* That night they left it in the shop and went to bed. *(They go out. The shop gets dark.)* Just like the night before, something happened. *(The elves come in and make two pairs of shoes. They depart.)* In the morning. . . . *(The shop gets light. The shoemaker and his wife come in.)*

SHOEMAKER: Come and look! Two pairs of shoes! They are very well made. Where did they come from? *(a knock)*

WIFE: I hope it is somebody wanting shoes. How did those fine, shiny shoes get here? Somebody will pay quite a lot for such shoes. *(The shoemaker opens the door.)*

WOMAN *(She comes in and sees the shoes.):* What fine shoes! They are very well made. I would like to buy them. *(She pays the shoemaker.)*

SHOEMAKER: Thank you! *(He opens the door. The woman departs.)* She gave me enough to buy leather for four pairs of shoes! *(The shoemaker and his wife laugh and hug.)*

WIFE: Where are the shoes coming from? I must know. Let's find out this very night. We will act as if we are going to bed, but instead we will hide and watch.

SHOEMAKER: Should we? Yes! We will hide and watch this very night! *(The curtain falls.)*

Act 2

STORYTELLER: That night the shoemaker and his wife cut leather for four pairs of shoes. Then they went to bed. Or so it seemed. But really they were hiding and watching. *(The curtain rises.)*

WIFE: The sun will soon be rising. Do you see anyone?

SHOEMAKER: Not yet. I don't see or hear a thing. Maybe . . . but look! Look there! *(Two elves come in. They begin to make shoes.)*

ELVES: Tap, tap, tap and shine.
Only elves make shoes this fine.

WIFE: Did you ever see such a thing! How small they are, but how fast they work. Look at their little fingers fly!

ELVES: All done! Time to run! *(They run out.)*

SHOEMAKER (*He and his wife go into the shop.*):
Look! There are four perfect pairs of
shoes. They are made from the leather
we cut. Those little men certainly do
fine work.

WIFE: Did you see their clothes? Their little
coats and shirts were so thin. They had
no shoes on their little feet! After all
they have done for us, we must do
something for them.

SHOEMAKER: I have some leather left. I will
make them each a pair of shoes!

WIFE: I have cloth. I will make them fine
shirts and warm coats of my best blue
cloth. (*They get the leather and cloth and
begin.*)

STORYTELLER: So the shoemaker made shoes to
fit the elves' feet. And his wife made
them coats and shirts. That night they
left these things for the elves to find.
(*The shoemaker and his wife put out the
clothes and shoes. Then they hide.*)

ELVES (*They come in and see the clothes. They jump up and down. Then they put on the clothes.*):

Now that we are well-dressed men,
We will not make fine shoes again!

(*They run out laughing. The shoemaker and his wife go to the door to watch them.*)

STORYTELLER: And no one ever saw the two elves again. But that was all right. For after that, the shoemaker and his wife did just fine for as long as they lived. (*The curtain falls.*)

Checking Comprehension and Skills

1. Could this story really happen? Why do you think so? (53)
2. What did the shoemaker and his wife need at the beginning of the story? (53)
3. How did they get what they needed? (53, 54)
●4. Were the shoemaker and his wife kind people? What details make you think so? (58)
5. Why did the shoemaker and his wife make clothes and shoes for the elves? (58)
●6. How did the elves know the clothes and shoes were for them? (58, 59)

Which word is best in the blank?

○7. The shoemaker made small shoes to ____ the elves' feet.

    fat   fine   fit

○8. Seven people are needed in the ____ of "The Elves and the Shoemaker."

    cast   case   cage

● Drawing conclusions
○ Phonics: Vowels

No Talking!

Here is a good game to play with a group of friends. Pick the name of a story you like. Do not tell your friends the name of the story. Start the game by acting out the name of the story. You can't talk! You can move your hands, legs, and head to help you act. The friend who can guess the name of your story first gets the next turn. Some names you can use are The Three Little Pigs, The Rabbit and the Turtle, The Little Red Hen, and The Magic Pot.

Puppets on Stage

Puppets are fun. You can make a puppet do what you want it to do. Which one of these puppets would you like to work?

Step by Step

Look at the pictures. What is the girl making? Yes, it's a sock puppet. What does she do first? next? last?

Sharpen Your Skills

It was not hard to learn how to make this puppet. You followed the pictures step by step. Sometimes you need to read about how to make something. You have to go step by step then too.

Think about what you are making. Think how it should look when you are done.

Look for clues that tell when to do each step. First, next, then, and last are clue words. Numbers can be clues too.

Now read to find out how to make an elephant puppet. Look for clue words to help you follow the steps.

First, put an old sock down flat and roll the sides in until they touch. That makes the elephant's nose. Next, tape the sides to hold them together. Then cut ears out of cloth. Sew the ears on. Last, sew on the buttons. They are the elephant's eyes.

1. Do you make the ears or the nose first?
2. What clue word tells you this?

You make the nose before the ears. The clue word first tells you this. Now read the steps again to see when to sew on the eyes.

3. When do you sew on the eyes?
4. What clue word tells this?

Next, follow the steps that tell you how to make a paper-bag puppet.

Make a Puppet

You will need

newspapers
string
a small paper bag
paint
brush
scissors

1. Crumple newspaper into a ball. The ball of crumpled paper should be about the size of a large apple.

2. Put the ball of crumpled paper into the bag.

3. Cut a piece of string. Make the string as long as the paper bag. Tie the string around the bag. Tie it just under the ball. Now your puppet has a head.

4. Use the scissors to cut two holes in the bag across from each other. The holes are for the puppet's hands.

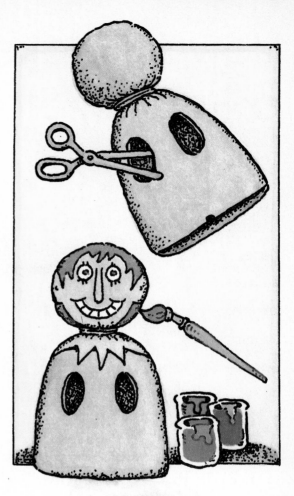

5. Paint a face and costume on the puppet.

Now your puppet is ready to use. Put your hand into the bag.
•Put your thumb through one hole.
•Put the finger next to your thumb into the puppet's head. You will have to push a hole into the crumpled newspaper.
•Put the next finger through the other hole.

Now you can work your puppet. Move your thumb. The puppet waves.

How to Make a Puppet Stage

You will need

a very large box
tape
paint
brush
scissors
sheets of paper

1. Cut a piece out of the front of the box at the top. This hole is the stage opening. It should look like this. Save the piece that is cut out.

2. Cut the lower half off the back of the box. The back of the box is across from the stage opening. This is the back of the stage. It is where you will go into the puppet stage.

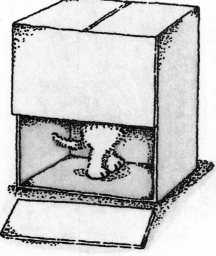

3. Paint a top for the stage. Use the piece of the box that you saved from the front. Tape it above the stage.

4. Paint the rest of the box. Half of this puppet stage is painted red. The other half is painted blue.

5. Paint scenery on the sheets of paper. Use a sheet for each piece of scenery. Tape the scenery in the box. Tape it across from the front stage opening. You can put up new scenery for each act in a play.

Now the stage is ready for a puppet show. Good luck!

Checking Comprehension and Skills

1. What are the things you will need to make a puppet? (66)

•2. What is the last thing you do to make a puppet? (67)

•3. What would happen if you painted the face on the bag before you did the first four steps?

4. How can you make your puppet wave? (67)

•5. What is the first thing you do to make a puppet stage? (68)

6. Why do you have to save the piece of the box that was cut from the front of the stage? (68, 69)

7. You can paint scenery on many sheets of paper. Why would you want to do this? (70)

8. What play would you like to make puppets and scenery for?

   Which word is best in the blank?
○9. Good ____ with your puppet show.
   luck   lock   lake

• Sequence: Steps in a process
○ Phonics: Vowels

The Three Ring Circus

The circus is the biggest show of all. All the acts seem to happen at once. Elephants do tricks in one ring. Trainers work with wild animals in cages in the other rings. Above the rings, people spin, roll, and swing. Clowns make everybody laugh. There is so much to see at a circus.

Burt's Dream

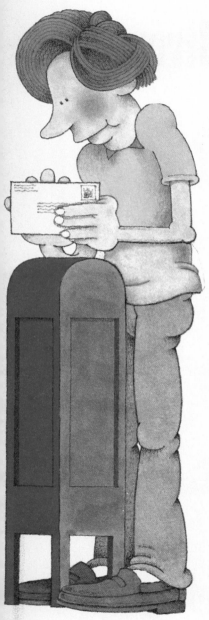

Burt dreamed of being a circus clown. But just dreaming would not make Burt a clown. He needed a plan.

First, Burt sent a note to a circus. He asked how he could learn to be a clown.

In a little while, Burt got an answer from the circus. The answer said the circus had a school for clowns. Many forms to fill in came with the answer. It took Burt a long time to fill in the forms. Then he sent the forms back to the circus.

Later, Burt got another answer from the circus. The circus liked what Burt said in the forms. The circus asked Burt to come to the clown school for a tryout.

Burt went to the clown school for the tryout. He was so good in his tryout that the circus asked him to go to their clown school.

Burt went to clown school. He learned all about being a clown.

There was a test on the last day of clown school. Each clown had to do an act to pass the test. After Burt's act, there was long and loud clapping. Burt had passed the test.

Burt no longer dreamed of being a clown. At last, he was a real clown.

Sharpen Your Skills

Clue words can help you figure out the order in which things happen in a story. <u>After</u>, <u>in a little while</u>, and <u>at last</u>, are some clue words.

1. What was the first thing Burt did to become a clown?
2. What was the last thing Burt had to do—fill in forms or do a clown act?

Think about the order in which things happen as you read the next story about Dizzy the dog.

What Do You Know?

Here is Dizzy the dog again. The circus trainer asked all the dogs to sit up. What do you think Dizzy did? You know Dizzy. You can guess that she did any trick but "sit up."

You can get more out of a story if you use what you know. You know something about dogs. You know it is hard to train them. Knowing that helped you when you read about Dizzy. It helped you see the fun in that story.

When you start to read a story, think:

• What is this story about?
• What do I know that will help me as I read this story?

When you read, use what you already know.

Section Three

TV World

It Takes More Than Actors

These children are watching a TV show. They see only the actors on the TV screen. The actors on the screen are only a small number of the people who work to put on a TV show.

Behind the Scenes

Many people are needed to put on a TV show. Some of these people are not actors. They don't work in front of the camera. They work behind the scenes.

This picture shows a woman who directs a TV show. She tells other workers on the show what to do. She keeps them working together to make a good show. She wants every scene to be just right.

Some workers run the TV cameras. Most shows use more than one camera. More than one person is needed to work the cameras. The woman who directs the show tells each camera person what kind of TV pictures to take.

Other people work the microphones. Microphones are needed for a TV show. They pick up all the sound on the show. The person directing the show tells the microphone workers when to use each microphone.

Other people are needed to work the lights. They make sure each scene is not too dark or too bright.

A show could not go on TV with only actors. The next time you watch TV, think about all the people who work to put on a TV show.

3.

4.

Sharpen Your Skills

Words such as she, them, and they are used in place of the names of people and things.
1. Read next to picture 1. Who is she?
2. Read next to picture 3. What are they?

As you read the next story, notice other words that are used in place of the names of people and things.

The Same But Different

by Kathryn Hallenstein

Rosa and Rita were twin sisters. They had the same birthday. They looked just like each other. They even laughed in the same way.

Sometimes being twins was hard for Rosa and Rita. People hardly ever knew which twin was Rosa and which was Rita. Even their best friends got them mixed up. People think that twins always like the same things. But Rosa and Rita were not as much the same as people thought they were.

On their way to school one day, Rosa and Rita saw a funny-looking van. It was in the school parking lot. The van had many kinds of fruit painted all over it. The name Squeezy Juice was on both sides.

The twins walked into their classroom. They saw their teacher, Mr. Jones, talking to a woman.

Mr. Jones asked the children to sit down. Then he said, "Children, meet Ms. Moy. Many of you probably saw Ms. Moy's van in the parking lot. Ms. Moy is from the Squeezy Juice Company. She brought us some new juice to try. Ms. Moy will tell you why she wants you to try Squeezy Juice for her company."

"Good morning, children," said Ms. Moy. "I'm here today to find out how you like our new juice. After you try the juice, I will ask you how you like it. Some camera and microphone workers came with me. They will be filming us as we talk. Then I'll pick the best film. The film will be used by our company as a TV commercial."

The children were so happy that they all talked at once. They thought it would be fun to be on TV.

"I'm sure, children, that you will tell Ms. Moy just what you think about the new juice," Mr. Jones said. "You must tell the truth."

Ms. Moy called the children two at a time into the other room. When they came back to their classroom, they laughed and talked about the juice.

"That orange juice was great!" said one girl.

"I said it was the sweetest juice I ever had," said another girl.

"I thought the flavor was good," said Rosa. "But I didn't think it was so sweet." She could not look at her sister's face.

"Thank you, girls, for your help," said Ms. Moy. "You can go back to your classroom now."

Soon Ms. Moy came back to the classroom. "You all did a very good job," she said. "I'm going to use Rosa and Rita in the TV commercial."

The boys and girls looked at each other. They knew everything that Rosa had said about the juice.

"Are you really going to use everything I said about the juice in your commercial?" asked Rosa.

"Everything you said was true," said Ms. Moy. "You did not pick out the orange flavor because we use many fruits. Oranges are only one of them.

"You said that the juice was not so sweet. You are right. Not a thing is added to make the juice sweeter. We only use fruit juice. So it's only as sweet as fruit is.

"You and Rita both said the truth about the juice even though you said different things. I guess twins who look the same can have different thoughts about something. That's why I picked you for the commercial."

Checking Comprehension and Skills

1. How were Rita and Rosa the same? (88)
2. How were they different? (93, 94)
•3. Rosa and Rita saw a funny-looking van. It was in the school parking lot.
   What was in the school parking lot?
4. What did Ms. Moy want the children to do? (91)
•5. Rosa thought about what Mr. Jones had said. He wanted the children to tell the truth.
   Who wanted the children to tell the truth?

What is the root word in each underlined word? What is the ending?

○6. There were <u>boxes</u> of juice in the room.
○7. Rosa and Rita put the two <u>glasses</u> down.

• Referents   ○ Structure: Endings

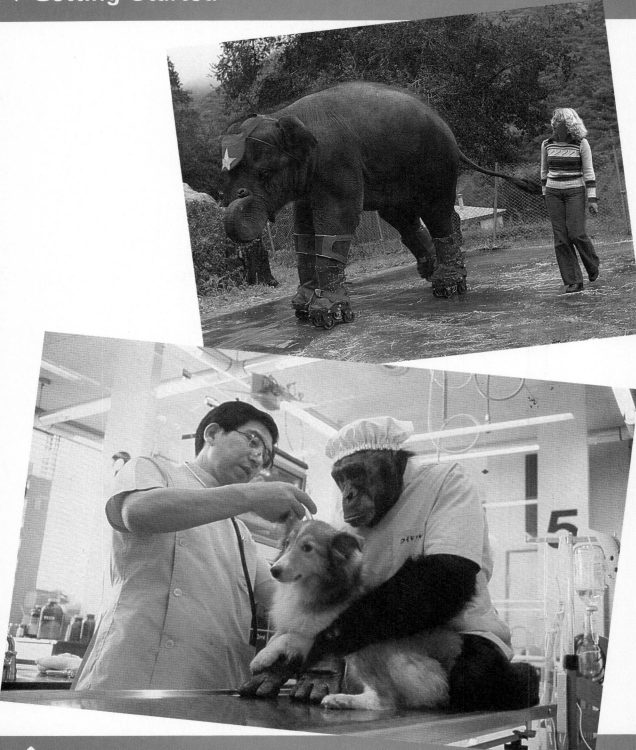

Animal Actors

Not all actors on TV are people. The animals in these pictures are acting. How do you think an animal gets to be an actor?

Root Words and Endings

The animals in the picture are on a TV game show. Look at the words that go with each animal. You know the first word in each pair. The second word has an ending added to it. Can you read all the words?

Sharpen Your Skills

Sometimes you will see root words that have endings added to them. What endings were added to <u>act</u>, <u>train</u>, <u>hard</u>, and <u>eat</u>? Yes, the endings <u>-ing</u>, <u>-s</u>, <u>-est</u>, and <u>-en</u> were added. Read the words with the endings.

Sometimes the spelling of a root word changes when an ending is added. Read the following words:

win	care	broke
winning	caring	broken

What ending was added to each root word? How did the spelling of each root word change?

Read the story. Name the root word and the ending for each underlined word.

I have always <u>liked</u> the TV show "Animal Game." <u>Sooner</u> or <u>later</u> it always makes me laugh. I laugh so hard that I have even <u>fallen</u> out of the chair I was <u>sitting</u> in.

Use what you have learned about root words and endings to help you as you read.

The Patsy Award

The Patsy Award is a prize given to the best animal actor every year. Some animals act in movies. Others work on TV shows and in commercials. The Patsy winner could be a dog or a cat or a wild animal. A raccoon in a movie once won a Patsy. Another winner was a camel. The people who train the animals work hard, so the award is for them too.

A group of people who care about animals give the Patsy Award. They watch animals and their trainers at work. They see how the animal and trainer work together. Because only animals that are treated well get Patsys, they watch for that also. They make sure animals are rewarded for their acting and are not hurt.

Then this group of people make a list. They list the animal actors they think are the best. One of the animals on the list will win the Patsy.

This list is given to another group of people. These are the people who will pick the winner. They watch movies of every animal on the list. They pick the best animal actor and its trainer. The Patsy Award is given to that animal and trainer.

Sharpen Your Skills

Connecting words like <u>and</u>, <u>or</u>, and <u>but</u> can bring two ideas together in one sentence.

1. Who is awarded the Patsy along with the animal?
2. The Patsy winner could be a dog or a cat or a wild animal. Does this mean three animals will win?

Read how animal actors are trained in "Gentle Jungle." Notice how connecting words can put two ideas together in one sentence.

Gentle Jungle

by Marianne von Meerwall

A School for Animals

Gentle Jungle is a school for animal actors. Animal actors are used in movies and on TV. Gentle Jungle trains animals for this work.

Almost every kind of animal in the world is trained at Gentle Jungle. You can find bears, lions, camels, and elephants at Gentle Jungle. Most of the animals are wild.

Gentle Jungle knows how to train wild animals. Trainers call it Affection Training. Affection Training is done with love, with patience, and by being kind.

Patience is a big part of Affection Training. Having patience means doing a lot of long and hard work. It takes about ten times longer to train animals by being kind to them than it does by hurting them. The animals at Gentle Jungle are not afraid of their trainers because they trust them. The animals learn because they want to please their trainers. The animals like their work.

The animals are trained to
do many different things. One
animal is trained to give a hug
and a kiss. The elephant is
trained to go fishing.

Does Affection Training really work? Indeed it does. Gentle Jungle has been training animals for many years. Its animals have won many Patsy Awards.

Even better than winning awards, the trainers have won the love of their animals. The animals trust them. Because of this trust, the trainers know that Affection Training is the best way to train animals.

A School for People

The trainers at Gentle Jungle are among the best in the world. Training animals is not their only work. They also teach other people how to work with wild animals.

Many students go to school at Gentle Jungle each year. These students want to learn about working with wild animals. Some want to be animal trainers or work in a zoo. Others want to be veterinarians or to take pictures of animals in all parts of the world.

At first, the students going to the school learn by watching the trainers. They see how the animals are taken care of. They see how the trainers treat the animals. They hear how the trainers talk to the animals.

Then the time comes for the students to work with the animals. They learn how to feed the animals and how to clean them. They learn how to work with them safely. They also learn how to train the animals.

Going to school at Gentle Jungle is work, but it's fun too. After all, there are not many schools where you can ride an elephant!

Checking Comprehension and Skills

1. What is "A School for Animals" mostly about? (102)
2. What three things are used to train animals with Affection Training? (103)
3. Why is Affection Training the best way to train animals? (105)
4. What is "A School for People" mostly about? (105)
•5. Name three things students at Gentle Jungle want to do when school is over. (106)
•6. Add the last part to this sentence.
   Going to school at Gentle Jungle is work, but ___.
7. Would you like to train a wild animal? What animal would you pick?

The students at Gentle Jungle see how the animals are <u>taken</u> care of.
○8. What ending was added to <u>take</u>?
○9. What spelling change was made?

• Connecting words
○ Structure: Endings

TV
Time

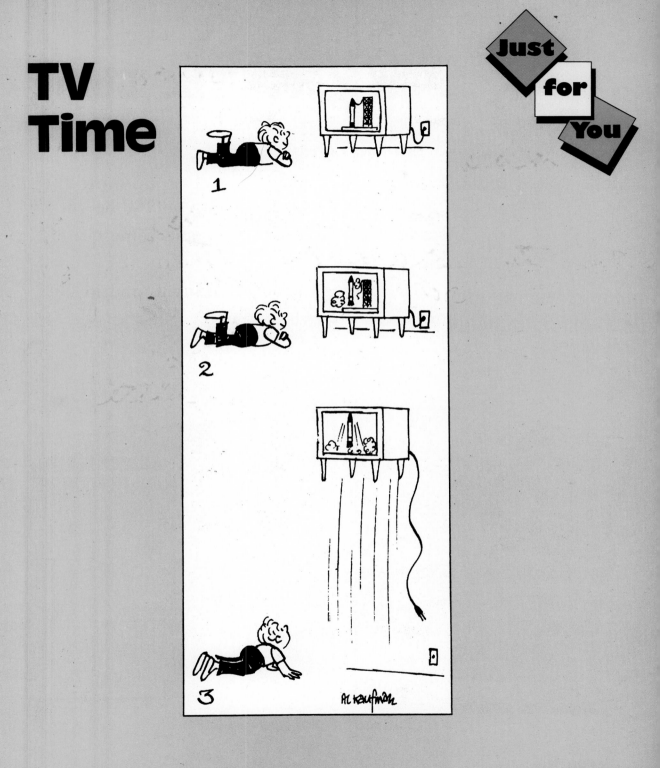

Jim Meets The Thing

by Miriam Cohen

When Jim saw The Thing on TV, he got scared. Maybe The Thing could come out of the TV!

He dreamed about it all night, and in the morning he was still scared.

But when he came to school, everybody was saying, "Did you see The Thing? I did! I did!"

Danny said, "It was great. I loved it! The Thing is so great. If it just does this with its eyes, the whole mountain falls down. But Mr. Fantastic can beat it!"

Ann said, "I liked it when The Thing ate the car with four people in it."

"Don't talk about it," Jim said.

"Oh, Jim is scared!" Danny yelled.

"No, I'm not," Jim said to everybody. But they all went on talking about The Thing.

At lunch, Jim didn't feel like eating. He was thinking about The Thing. Why was he the only one in his class who got scared?

After lunch Paul said, "Come on, Jim. Let's play."

"Let's play a TV game," said Ann. "I'll be Jungle Girl. Paul can be Ice Man."

Danny said, "I'll be Mr. Fantastic."

"Who are you going to be, Jim?" Sara asked. Jim looked down at his shoes. He didn't feel like playing. He was still scared.

Ann started to run and jump. She jumped in front of Sara. "Don't try to get away! I'm Jungle Girl. I can stop you!" she yelled.

Jim walked away. He didn't want to play.

Paul was trying to turn everybody to ice. He worked very hard. Danny jumped up. "Mr. Fantastic!" he yelled.

"Stop that, Danny!" Sara was angry. "I was eating my apple with very little bites and you made me make a mistake!"

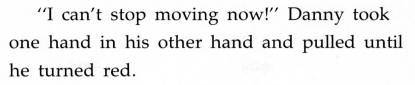

"I can't stop moving now!" Danny took one hand in his other hand and pulled until he turned red.

"There is something walking on you, Danny," said Sara.

"There is not," said Danny. Then he said, "What is it?"

"It's a big bug," said Sara.

"HELP! HELP! Get it off!" Danny yelled.

"I'm not going to touch it," said Ann.

Paul said, "Its legs are like green sticks. Its eyes are like the lights in front of a car."

"That bug is going to bite you!" said Sara.

"Run, Danny!" yelled Paul.

But Jim said, "Stand still, Danny." He took a piece of paper and put it under the bug. Then, with care, he lifted the bug off Danny.

Everybody moved back. "Get it! Step on it!" they screamed.

"No," said Jim.

And Paul said, "How would you like it if something big stepped on you?"

Jim took the bug to a tree and put it on the ground.

Jim walked back to the kids.

"Boy, you were brave. You must be Danger Man!" Sara said to Jim.

Ann said, "I'm brave too. But you know what I <u>am</u> scared of? Sometimes I think animals are under my bed."

"I don't think they are," said Sara.

Danny added, "I used to be scared of the dark all the time, but now I'm not."

And Paul said, "When I was little, I was scared. I thought Ice Man was bad. But now I know he is good."

Jim jumped up and did a flip. Everybody got scared sometimes. But now he was brave. Danger Man could beat The Thing!

Books to Read

Paul and His Little-Big Dog by Kathy Darling

Paul takes good care of his new puppy. The puppy grows and grows and grows until it's bigger than Paul.

Louie by Ezra Jack Keats

Louie hardly ever talks until he meets Gussie the puppet. Learn how a green string brings Louie and Gussie together.

Madge's Magic Show by Mike Thaler

Madge says she will pull a rabbit out of her hat. Jimmy Smith says she can't do it. Madge pulls some surprising things out of her hat.

Barkley by Syd Hoff

Barkley is a circus dog, but he is too old to do his act. Find out how Barkley gets back into the circus.

Section Four
Sisters, Brothers, and Others

Being the Oldest

The boy in the picture is the oldest of the children in his family. He likes being the oldest. He can go to bed later than the other two children. He goes to school, but the other children are too little. Being oldest also means he has more jobs to do. It means he must help take care of his sister and the new baby. What are other things the oldest one in a family can do?

Hello, It's Me

Ruth's mother answered the phone. "Hello."

"Hello," said Ruth. "It's me."

"Ruth, where are you?" Her mother sounded surprised. "I thought you were here at home."

"I'm phoning from Mrs. Ott's next door," said Ruth. "It was the only way I could think of to talk to you. I need your help with my schoolwork so I won't do it wrong. You said you were too busy with the baby to help me."

"Come home," said her mother. "Let's talk."

Ruth ran home.

"You don't have any time for me," said Ruth sadly. "Can't you quit doing things for the baby for a while?"

"I can't quit," said her mother. "You can't quit doing things for a new baby. A baby is not able to do things on his own. But you, clever girl, are able to do almost everything on your own."

"Yes, I guess so," said Ruth. "But I'm not able to do some of my schoolwork so it won't be wrong."

"You know I have to take care of the baby first," said her mother. "Sometimes that makes you feel bad. But we can be sure to spend some time together every day. So from now on you won't have to phone home."

Ruth started to laugh.

Sharpen Your Skills

Characters are the people in a story. What a character does or says tells you what kind of person that character is.

1. Who are the characters in this story?
2. Why did Ruth phone her mother? How did Ruth feel about her mother being busy with the baby?

Find out how the girl in the next story feels about being the oldest.

The Oldest Kid

by Elaine Knox-Wagner

Ever since I was born, I have been the oldest kid.

It's not fair.

Being oldest means I got to our house first. It means my room and toys and Dad and Mom were all mine—until my brother came. Then he moved into my room with me. I had to let him play with my things. EVERYTHING. Even the big map on my bedroom wall. (He ate half of the map.)

Being oldest means I have to be perfect. When I want another ride on the horse at the park, Dad says, "No, just one today." I climb off the horse right away. My brother screams and hangs on to his horse so hard my dad has to PEEL him off. If I did that, I would probably get traded in like our old car.

Being oldest means I should do what the teacher tells me and get A's. I should make my bed and say "Thank you" and "Please." It means I should not hurt little kids or do ONE thing wrong.

It's not fair.

On warm Sundays, we have picnics at Grandma and Grandpa's. The kids eat first. Only ten fit at the picnic table.

Guess who's the oldest cousin? Guess who makes one more than ten? Guess who eats later?

At last Sunday's picnic, I got mad. There I was, about to starve.

"I want a place at the picnic table this Sunday," I tell my grandma.

"You can eat later," she says.

"But I want to eat now," I say. "I'm starving."

"You won't starve," says my dad, feeding my brother. "Go talk to your grandpa for a while."

I take a bun so I won't starve.

Grandpa is repairing his car. It's very old. He spends a lot of time repairing his car. Grandma says it is his first love. She means he really likes it.

"I hate being the oldest kid," I tell him. "It's not fair."

He glances up and hands me a screwdriver.

"I can't even eat with the other kids," I say. "There is no room for me."

He glances up again and hands me a wrench.

"I'm a kid too," I say.

"Quite right," he says. "Would you aim this flashlight right over there?"

I put the screwdriver in my hat. Then I aim the flashlight so he can see.

"Now aim it over here. Just as I thought,"
he says. "Wrench?" I put the flashlight down
and hand him the wrench.

"Screwdriver?" He takes it from my hat.
He clamps the wrench around a nut. He starts
to use the screwdriver with his other hand.

"Well," he says. "I can't do both at once."

"I can help," I say.

He glances up. "Fine. You hold this
wrench. Don't let it slip."

Grandpa turns the screwdriver. I use both
hands to hold the wrench still. Just when I
think I can't hold it any longer, Grandpa says,
"That's it, Pal. We did it."

We put our things away and get cleaned up. "Oh, Grandma," Grandpa calls. "We are going out for a spin. We have to test this repair job."

All the cousins who can walk and talk jump up from the table. They run over to us.

"Me, too! Me, too!" they yell.

"Not this time, kids," Grandpa says. "Not this time."

He starts the car and slowly backs away. The cousins run after us.

"You think you are so great," my one cousin yells at me. "Just because you are the oldest, you get to do EVERYthing."

Grandpa says, "You can have your turn next Sunday."

As we ride along, I don't talk so Grandpa can hear the motor. We ride around the lake and out to the country.

"Runs like a top," he says at last. "We did quite a good job on it, Pal."

He lets me turn the knob to the radio as we head back to the house. Ever since I was born, I have been the oldest kid. It's hardly ever fair. But sometimes it feels fair.

Checking Comprehension and Skills

- 1. What character is this story mostly about?
     (122–128)
- 2. How does the girl feel about being the oldest
     kid? Why? (122–124)
  3. Why was the girl mad at the picnic? (124)
  4. How did the girl's grandpa get her to quit
     complaining? (125–128)
- 5. How did the cousin who yelled at the girl
     feel about her being oldest? (127)
  6. At the end of the story, why did the girl feel
     better about being the oldest? (128)
  7. Could this story really happen?
  8. Do you think being the oldest would be fun
     or not? Why do you think so?

- ○ 9. Which word begins with the same sound as
        new?
        The girl turned the radio knob.
- ○10. Which word begins with the same sound as
        ride?
        I held the wrench with both hands.

- Story Elements: Character
- ○ Phonics: Initial digraphs

A Family Outing

This family is getting ready for a day at the sea. Each person in the family is doing something to help. They know they will all have fun. They are happy to help each other.

Batter Up

Amy's older brother Ed held up the ball and bat. "How well can you hit?" he asked.

"Not well," said Amy. "I can run fast and throw hard, but I'm not much of a hitter. I could use your help."

"Well, step up to the plate, batter," Ed said. "I'll throw you some fast balls. I'll make you a better hitter in no time."

"Great! But I have to shop first," said Amy. "Mom asked me to get some things for dinner since she has to work late. Can we do it when I get back?"

"I can't, Amy," Ed said. "I have to be back at work soon. I won't even be here for dinner."

Amy felt crushed. Ed always seemed to be working when Amy needed his help. She could be a much better hitter with his help. Then Amy had an idea. She went to find her little brother Tim.

"Tim," she said. "Mom needs these things for dinner. If you will go shopping for me now, I'll wash the car for you on Sunday."

Tim said he would.

Amy ran back out to Ed. "I'm ready!" she said, picking up the bat.

"All right!" Ed yelled. "Batter up!"

Sharpen Your Skills

When you read a story, think about what the characters want. Then find out if they get what they want and how they get it.
1. What did Amy want?
2. How did Amy get what she wanted?

Larry wants to please his uncle in the next story, "Do Me a Favor." Find out if Larry is able to do what he wants.

Do Me a Favor

by Tom Llewellyn

As soon as Larry got off the school bus, he saw the car in front of his house.

"Uncle Brad!" Larry thought. He ran home as fast as he could and went around behind the house. He ran in the back door.

His mother looked up and said, "Hello."

"Hello," he said, out of breath. "Is that Uncle Brad's car out in front? Is he here for a visit?"

"Yes," said his mother. "But he has an awful cold and he is sleeping. Would you take care of him for a while? If he wakes up and wants something, would you get it for him?"

"Sure," said Larry. Larry wanted to please his uncle in every way.

"Oh, Larry, Uncle Brad brought you something," called his father. "He can give it to you before dinner."

Uncle Brad's job took him all over the world. When he visited them, he always brought Larry something from a far-off land.

Larry had dozens of shells and stones from his uncle. He had given Larry dozens of things. His uncle had brought him maps, pictures, and dozens of books.

On his last visit, he brought Larry a ship model to put together. Larry had done a lot of work on it already. His uncle would be pleased. Larry went to his room to work on the model while his uncle was sleeping.

The Switch

by Kay Hall

"I've had it with being an only child," said Jenny Norris. "An only child has to do too many things around the house."

Jenny's best friend, Rose Miller, shook her head. "It would be nice to have different jobs to do," said Rose. "My only job is to help with dinner. It sounds easy, but do you know how much food a family as big as mine eats? Mountains! I would switch places with you any day."

"That's a great idea!" said Jenny. "Let's ask if we can switch places for every Tuesday. You take my place in my family, and I'll take your place in yours."

Each family said the girls could switch places every Tuesday.

On Tuesday morning the girls switched places.

Rose liked being at the Norrises' house. She was really going to enjoy this Tuesday. For one thing, there were no little brothers and a sister around asking for things. She went to Jenny's room. No little child could bother her there. There was lots of time to read. "This is the best Tuesday I've had in a long time," thought Rose. "I love having time just for me."

Jenny enjoyed being at the Millers' house too. Brothers or a sister were always around to talk to. Eating lunch was more like a circus. After lunch, everybody ran around doing different things. "How could Rose not like all this fun?" thought Jenny.

After lunch at the Norrises' house, things were different. Rose had to wash all the glasses and plates. When it was time for house cleaning, she had to help dust and sweep.

At the Millers' house, Jenny was helping to get dinner ready. She peeled and sliced six apples. Mrs. Miller was making applesauce.

"This is a nice start," said Mrs. Miller. "But where are the rest of the apples? You need to peel all the apples in the bag for the applesauce, Jenny. There are a lot of us."

So Jenny peeled and sliced for over an hour. "I don't even like applesauce," Jenny thought.

Later that night, the two friends met again.

"Let's forget this switching," said Rose. "I like having only one job to work on. And I miss my sister and brothers even though they do ask me to do a lot of things."

"I want to switch back too," said Jenny. "I've peeled and sliced enough apples to last me a year! I guess I like being an only child better. This switching was not the best idea after all."

"I guess not," said Rose. "I thought it was a great idea at first. Well, switching places showed us we were really happy in our own homes all along."

The Nut Hut Contest

by Kate Holland

The nights were getting longer. The air was getting colder. Winter was almost here. It was also the day of the Nut Hut Contest.

The Chipmunk family worked together to build a Nut Hut. The Nut Hut held all the nuts they would need during the winter. Every year they held a contest. The chipmunk who could bring in the most nuts would be King or Queen of the Nut Hut for a year.

On the day of the contest, each member of the Chipmunk family lined up. Boxer Chipmunk was pulling his pouches. He was trying to make them bigger so he could carry more nuts. Bingo Chipmunk had put large stones in her pouches for days. She thought the stones would stretch her pouches and make them bigger.

PeeWee Chipmunk was the last to get in line. PeeWee was the youngest in the Chipmunk family. He had on big black boots and a hat. "Who are you supposed to be today, PeeWee?" asked Bingo.

"I'm the Great Hunter of Nuts," said PeeWee.

"Well, you aren't going to get any nuts that way," said Boxer. "You can't run fast in those big boots. You can't see well in that hat."

Just then the contest started. Old and young chipmunks raced here and there. They raced everywhere.

At last the contest was over. It was time to learn which chipmunk won.

The chipmunks took the nuts from their pouches. Boxer had eight nuts! Bingo had nine nuts! When PeeWee's turn came, he took only two nuts from his pouches. Then he took two nuts from each boot. Next, he took four nuts from his hat. PeeWee had ten nuts! PeeWee was the newest and youngest Nut Hut King!

Checking Comprehension and Skills

1. In the beginning of the story, how did Jenny and Rose feel about their own families? (148)

2. At the end of the story, how did Jenny and Rose feel about switching places? (151)

•3. Is "The Switch" a realistic story or a fantasy? Why?

4. What is "The Nut Hut Contest" all about?

   a. Nuts are good for everybody.

   b. PeeWee Chipmunk got to be the Nut Hut King because he found the most nuts.

5. What did PeeWee want to do in "The Nut Hut Contest?" (152)

6. How did he get to do what he wanted? (154)

•7. Is "The Nut Hut Contest" a realistic story or a fantasy? Why?

    What are the two syllables in the underlined word?

○8. Every <u>member</u> of the Chipmunk family got in line.

• Realism and fantasy
○ Structure: Syllables

The TV in Your Head

Did you ever see anyone who had a TV in his head? The boy in the picture has one. He uses it to see pictures of what he reads. That way, he gets more from each story.

You can do it too. Here is how. Think about the story you just read, "The Nut Hut Contest." How do you think Boxer and Bingo Chipmunk looked with all those nuts in their pouches? Close your eyes. Picture the chipmunks, just as if they were on a TV show in your head. How do their faces look—fat? Does the picture you see make you laugh?

Next time you read a story, use the TV in your head. Picture what you are reading. You will get more from what you read.

Section Five
Fly Away

You Do It Too

by Margaret Langford

I can spread my wings
Like a bird in the sky,
And fly round in rings—
Would you like to try?

A Boy Who Flew

Long, long ago a boy named Icarus and his father were trapped in a land far from home. They wanted to get away. The sea lay all around the land, but they had no boat. The only way they could get away was to fly across the sea like the birds.

Icarus's father watched the sea birds from a steep cliff that lay by the sea. He saw how the sea birds moved their wings. Some of the birds dropped feathers. Icarus's father picked up the feathers that lay on the ground. Then he started to make two pairs of wings.

Icarus's father laid out the feathers on the ground. He laid the larger feathers above the smaller feathers. When the feathers were all laid out, he used beeswax to hold them together. The wings looked like birds' wings. Icarus and his father climbed the cliff. His father put on a pair of wings. He put the other pair of wings on Icarus.

He warned Icarus, "Don't fly near the sun. If you fly too close to the sun, the sun's heat will melt the beeswax. Then the feathers will drop off. You will fall into the sea. Please, don't forget my warning."

Icarus and his father flew off the cliff. Icarus enjoyed flying so much that he forgot his father's warning. He flew up closer and closer to the sun. Soon the beeswax melted and the feathers dropped off the wings. Just as his father had warned, Icarus fell into the sea. He was not ever seen again.

Sharpen Your Skills

Details are small pieces of information. Details help you picture what you read.

1. What was used to make the wings?
2. What happened to Icarus's wings when he flew too close to the sun?

Learn why the King was afraid to visit the people in "The King's Balloon."

"It's our king! It's our king!" the child cried. All the people ran over to see their king.

"Are you hurt?" asked an old man, helping King Myron to his feet.

"No, I don't think so," said King Myron.

"Then welcome to our carnival!" said the old man. All the people at the carnival clapped.

Later that night when the King's family came to meet him, they found a very happy king.

"I'm having such a wonderful time," said King Myron. "Just look at all the friends I have made. I won't ever be shy again!"

Checking Comprehension and Skills

1. What did King Myron want? (162)
2. How did King Myron get what he wanted? (168)
●3. How did the balloon get up in the air? (164)
●4. What did the king do as the balloon started to come down? (166)
5. How did King Myron feel when he was about to land in the carnival? (167)
6. King Myron was no longer shy when the story was over. Why not? (168)
7. What could you do to help a shy person feel less shy?

   Which word is best in the blank?
○8. In the morning a ____ of sun peeped into the courtyard.
   road   ran   ray
○9. "Oh, my!" wailed King Myron. "The rope has come ____."
   foal   free   farm

● Details
○ Phonics: Vowels

Up, Up, and Away

What's it like to fly in a hot air balloon? People are amazed by how it feels. They say it feels as if the world is moving, but the balloon is standing still.

Watching the balloons go up is also amazing. The balloons come in many colors. The sky fills with color as they go up. The colors look very bright as the balloons float up in the sky.

Finding the Main Idea and Supporting Details

What does the picture show? Can you tell in one or two words? Yes, it shows balloons. In one sentence, what could you say about the kinds of balloons in the picture? You could say, "There are many kinds of balloons."

Sharpen Your Skills

You found the most important idea in the picture. When you read, you need to find the most important idea in a paragraph. Here is how to do it.

1. Find the **topic.** The topic is what the whole paragraph is mostly about. You can tell what it is in one or two words.

2. Look for the **main idea.** That is the most important idea about the topic. Many times one sentence tells the main idea.
3. Look for **details.** Details are sentences that tell more about the main idea.

Look for the main idea in this paragraph:

There are many kinds of balloons. There are round balloons. There are long balloons. There are animal balloons too.

1. In a word or two, what is the paragraph mostly about? That is the topic.
2. Which sentence tells the most important idea about the topic? It is the main idea.
3. What details tell more about the main idea?

Answer the same questions about this paragraph:

Balloons can be big enough to carry a person up in the air. They can be big enough to lift a horse! They can be small enough to fit in your hand. Balloons come in all sizes.

Main idea sentences will help you to find the meaning in "Hot Air Ballooning" better.

Hot Air Ballooning

by Anne V. McGravie

What makes a hot air balloon fly? It will fly because hot air rises. Hot air is lighter than cold air. The balloon is filled with cold air on the ground. Several people hold the balloon at the opening right above the basket. They flap the balloon to let air in. The balloon begins to fill out. The cold air in the balloon is then heated.

A **burner** is used to heat the air. The burner hangs under the balloon. When the air is hot enough, the balloon lifts off the ground. The balloon will float in the air as long as the air in the balloon is warm. When the air begins to get cold, the balloon starts to go down. Then the burner must heat up the air again for the balloon to go up.

burner, a machine that makes a flame.

Did You Know?
The first
living beings
to fly in a
balloon were a
duck, a sheep,
and a chicken.

Hot air balloons flow along on the wind because they can't be steered. The wind blows in different directions at different heights. When the balloon first goes up, the pilot watches for wind directions. She wants to find a wind that is blowing in the direction she wants. The pilot notes the heights of these winds. Then the pilot lifts the balloon to the height she wants. She may have to heat the air in the balloon again. Or, she may have to drop the balloon to the height she wants. She drops the balloon by letting the air in the balloon get cold.

crew, any group of people working together.

A **crew** on the ground is needed for a balloon flight. Crew members help the balloon take off and land. When the pilot is ready to take off, she says, "Hands off!" Then the crew sets the balloon free for the flight. The crew chases the balloon in a car or truck. The crew knows where the pilot wants to go. They learn which roads to take. They try to keep the balloon in view from their car. That way, the crew can help when the pilot is ready to land the balloon.

Landing a hot air balloon is not always easy. Sometimes the pilot can't land where she wants to. She may not be able to find the right wind direction. Then the pilot has to land without the crew. After she lands, she telephones a number that was given out before the flight. She tells the person on the telephone where she is. If the crew members can't see the balloon, they call the same person. They learn where the pilot landed. Then they go and help the pilot. They pack up the balloon and the basket so everything will be ready for another day of hot air ballooning.

Did You Know?
The first crossing of the Pacific Ocean in a balloon was made in 1981.

A Balloon Rally

by Monica Gallagher

Would you like to see a great number of balloons take off at one time? Where could you see such an amazing thing? At a balloon rally, of course!

A balloon rally takes place when many people who own balloons get together. A rally is held so that these people can talk about ballooning and fly together. Balloon games may be part of a rally.

One balloon game is "Hare and Hounds." In "Hare and Hounds" one balloon is the Hare. The Hare balloon goes up first. In a little while, all the other balloons go up together. They are the Hounds. The Hound balloons try to find the Hare balloon which tries to hide. The Hare balloon will fly for about an hour before it lands. The winner is the Hound balloon that finds the Hare balloon and lands the closest to it.

Another balloon game is "Hit the Mark."
It is a game in which a balloon pilot tries to hit
a mark with a bag of sand. The mark is a
large cloth X placed on the ground. The pilot
tries to fly over the X and drop the bag. The
pilot whose bag lands closest to the X wins.

Both "Hare and Hounds" and "Hit the
Mark" test the skills of balloon pilots. It is
not always easy to fly a balloon to the right
place. The pilot has to think and act fast.

Learning to fly a balloon takes a lot of time and patience. But balloon pilots and crews would not have it any other way. It is a hobby that is enjoyed by working together. And once up in the air, there is always that feeling of being as free as the birds.

Checking Comprehension and Skills

1. Hot air balloons can't be steered. How does the pilot get to where she wants to go? (175)
2. How do crew members help in a hot air balloon flight? (176)
●3. What is the topic of the second paragraph on page 178—a balloon rally or games?
●4. Which sentence in that paragraph tells the main idea about the topic? (178)
●5. What details tell more about the main idea? (178)

○6. Which word has the same last sound as the word she?

fly   go   hobby

● Main idea and supporting details
○ Phonics: Vowels

Balloon Friends

It's fun to find balloon friends. Here is what you do.

Write your name, your street name and number, and the city and state where you live on a piece of paper. Then write, "If you find this balloon, please write to me." Fit the paper into the balloon.

Have the balloon filled with helium. The helium will make the balloon go up in the air. Then tie the balloon with a string. Hold on to the string. Take the balloon out to an open place like a big parking lot and let it go up in the sky. Some helium-filled balloons have floated as far away as three states. Soon you may hear from a new friend from far away.

Airborne

These people are really airborne! They are flying on fast-moving air in a place called the Aerodium. What is it like to be airborne? It's like something a person has not ever done before, but always wanted to do.

The Aerodium

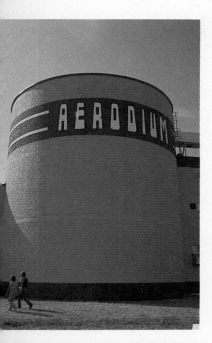

The building looks like a big soft drink can. It's about five floors tall, and it's orange in color. Around the top there is a black stripe. On the stripe is painted the word Aerodium.

The Aerodium is a place where people can play games in the air. How can you play games in the air? By flying! But how can you fly on your own? The answer to that can be found under your feet.

The floor of the Aerodium is different from most floors. It looks like a large wire screen. It springs up and down, and you can see through it. Under the floor you can see a machine. The machine has a very large fan on it. When the machine is turned on, the fan blows air up through the floor to the top of the building.

The fan moves the air at different speeds. When the fan spins very fast, the air blows hard. The faster the fan spins, the harder the air blows. The harder the air blows, the stronger it is. When the air is strong enough to lift you, you can fly!

Sharpen Your Skills

The **topic** of a paragraph is what the whole paragraph is about. The **main idea** of a paragraph is the most important idea about the topic. **Details** are small pieces of information that tell more about the main idea.

1. What is the topic of the first paragraph?

    a. The Aerodium   b. a black stripe

2. Which sentence tells the most important idea given about the topic?

3. What are some details that tell more about the main idea?

As you read "You Can Fly," learn why a person puts on the right clothes to fly in the Aerodium.

You Can Fly

by Alan Bickley

The person who owns the Aerodium feels that almost anyone, young or old, can learn to fly. Trainers teach people of different ages and sizes the skills of riding on air. But the first rule to learn is to be safe.

Being safe begins with putting on the right clothes. If you want to fly in the Aerodium, you must put on a suit that's like a balloon, glasses, a hard hat, and soft shoes. People who fly for the first time almost always take a spill or two. Their knees and elbows need to be protected. So you must also put on knee and elbow pads. The knee and elbow pads are an extra way of being safe. These clothes and pads help keep you from being hurt.

The suit not only protects you, it also helps you fly. It has a lot of room, and the arms have holes covered with nets that let air in. The air blown up from the machine comes through these holes. In less than a second, the suit is blown up like a balloon. The blown-up balloon suit will also keep you from being hurt in a fall.

The walls of the Aerodium are different from most walls. The walls are covered with padding. The padding is soft enough to protect you from a spill or a hard knock. The padded walls are in different bands of colors. Each color is a certain number of feet from the floor. You can tell how far up you are flying by the band of color around you.

A trainer is in the room at all times. The trainer will show you how to go up and how to come down.

When you are ready to start, the machine will be turned on. The trainer will help you slide into the flow of air. It's just like going into a pool for a swim. The balloon suit will catch the air, and you will be flying on your own.

The secret of flying in the Aerodium is how you use your arms and legs. To go up, you must open your arms and legs in the shape of an X. To come down, you must bring your arms and legs close together. To move to the front, you must keep your arms stretched out and pull them back and up a little. For most people, it's easy after the trainer helps them.

You must learn to come down safely. It's an easy trick, but you must do it slowly and with care. If you don't, you will come down too fast. To come down safely, you bend each knee and lift your arms. You have to learn to come down safely before the machine is turned on.

People have always dreamed of being able to fly on their own. Some people have flown in balloons. You might fly one day in a suit that looks like a balloon in a place like the Aerodium.

Checking Comprehension and Skills

1. Why must you put on a balloon suit in the Aerodium? (187)
2. Put these steps in the right order for flying in the Aerodium. (186–187)
   a. The machine is turned on.
   b. You put on the right clothes.
   c. The balloon suit fills with air.
3. Why are the walls of the Aerodium in different bands of color? (187)
●4. What is the topic of the first paragraph on page 189?
●5. Which sentence in that paragraph tells the main idea about the topic?
●6. What details tell more about the main idea?
7. In what ways are hot air ballooning and flying in the Aerodium alike?
8. Would you like to fly in a place like the Aerodium? Why or why not?

   Which word in the sentence has the same sound as blown?
○9. Some people have flown up and down.

● Main idea and supporting details   ○ Phonics: Vowels

How Am I Doing?

Suppose you flew a hot air balloon. As you flew, you might wonder, "How am I doing?" You would want to check to make sure you were doing everything right.

When you read, it is also a good idea to stop and ask, "How am I doing?" You can catch your own mistakes. Stop and think:

- Does this make sense?
- Would it help to read some parts again?
- Do I know all the words? Should I go back to figure some words out?

Everybody who reads makes some mistakes, but you can catch many mistakes on your own. Try using the questions above and see.

Section Six
Only in America

George Washington

The President of the United States of America is the person who is head of our country. George Washington was the first President of the United States of America. He was loved by the people in America.

There is a famous story about George Washington when he was a young boy. It is said he cut down his father's tree. When his father asked how it happened, George said "Father, I cannot tell a lie. I cut down your tree." People felt George Washington would always tell the truth.

A Visit to Mount Vernon

Peg, Molly, and their mom went in the gate. "This is Mount Vernon," said Peg. "George Washington, a famous President of the United States, lived here. He was the first President of the United States of America."

"How do you know?" Molly asked. Molly was four and sometimes asked things like that.

"I learned it in school," said Peg, "when we read about all of America's Presidents."

The front of Washington's big house looked out over the Potomac River. Near the big house were many small buildings. "This is a horse barn," Peg said. "In Washington's time people rode horses. They didn't have cars."

"Did you hear that in school?" Molly asked.

Peg said "Yes," then she took Molly to another building. "This is the kitchen," she said. "See the pots and pans?"

She showed her the icehouse where the people used to keep ice. "Down there," she said, "is a famous building. It's the little schoolhouse used by children at Mount Vernon."

Front of
Mount Vernon

Did You Know?
Washington was called "The Father of His Country." He cared for a new America just as a father cares for his growing child.

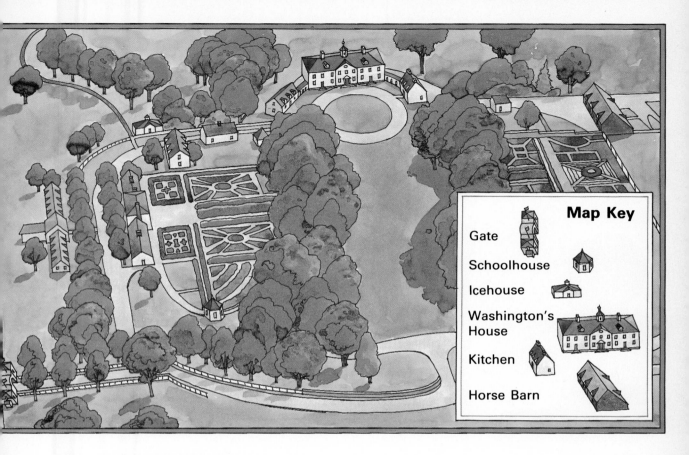

Map Key

Gate

Schoolhouse

Icehouse

Washington's House

Kitchen

Horse Barn

Sharpen Your Skills

A **map** shows you where places are.

1. Imagine you are at the horse barn. Which building is closer—the kitchen or the icehouse?

2. Is the schoolhouse closer to the gate or to Washington's house?

Use the map in the next story to see where a parade started and where it went.

George Washington Saves the Day

by Nancy Ross Ryan

The day was Tuesday. It was the day before the George Washington Birthday Parade. The teacher had put Dan in charge of costumes. Dan had always been good at taking charge.

Some children in the third grade were going to dress as Pilgrims. Others would dress as the people in George Washington's time. The children had made paper hats, jackets, and dresses. Some Pilgrims would carry Thanksgiving baskets. The baskets would be filled with squash made of bright paper. Other Pilgrims would carry paper muskets.

Dan would be dressed as George Washington in a blue paper jacket. He would march first. The children, dressed in costumes of George Washington's time, would follow Dan.

The turkey, a boy covered in brown paper feathers, would be next. The Pilgrims would follow the turkey.

The boys and girls in Dan's class had warned him, "Close the window before you go out!" Then they had all gone to lunch. But Dan was so busy, he forgot to close the window. Then it rained. Now the paper costumes, squash, and muskets were all wet. "They'll be angry," Dan thought. "I'd be angry too if I came back after lunch and found my costume was all wet. All because you-know-who didn't close the window."

But now the Pilgrims' hats were out of shape. The paper squash had gone flat. The paper muskets were a mess. The turkey's feathers were falling off. Dan's costume had spots on it. "Some parade!" Dan thought. There would not be time to make new costumes by Wednesday. It had taken days to make these.

"George Washington," he said. "You've gotten into a very tough spot. You had better think fast. They'll be back soon."

While Dan was thinking about his tough problem, his teacher was walking across the playground. She was thinking about Wednesday. "I'd feel better if we had gone over the plans one last time," she thought.

In the classroom, the teacher saw the open window and wet costumes. But Dan held up a message on a big sign. His teacher read it and grinned.

When Dan's class came back from lunch, they were not happy. "Now we can't march in the parade," they said. "There will be people watching the parade. They'll laugh at us."

The teacher gave a sign for the class to stop talking. "Now, now," she said. "The parade must go on. I think Dan's message will help. You know our class was picked to start the parade. Dan will carry his message in front of our class."

The third grade felt better when they read the message on Dan's sign.

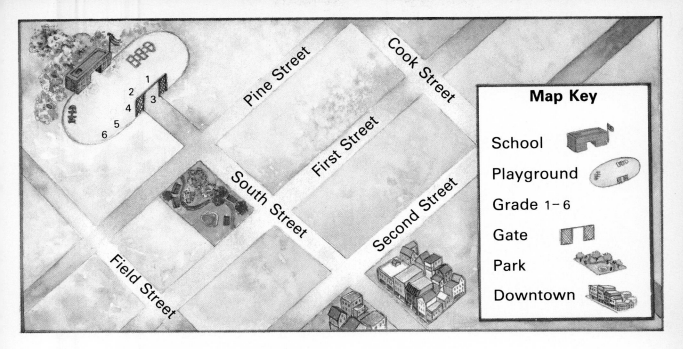

By Wednesday morning, the costumes were dry. But they still looked bad. The third grade got in line on the playground. The turkey's feathers were missing. The Pilgrims had flat paper squash and messed-up muskets. They didn't look much like the Pilgrims on the first Thanksgiving.

It would be tough for Dan too. With spots on his jacket, he didn't look much like George Washington. But Dan held up his sign.

The third grade marched out the front gate of the playground on to South Street. They were followed by all the other grades. They marched down South Street to the park.

At the park, a police captain on horseback saw Dan's sign and stopped. He said to Dan's teacher, "I'd be proud of those children if I were you. You've got a great class here!"

"You've got a great horse," Dan said.

The captain picked Dan up, sign and all. Then the captain said, "Charge!" And his horse started down South Street. The children followed Dan and the captain downtown.

Downtown, people were lined up to watch the parade. All of the people could read the message on Dan's sign. It said: "I am George Washington. I cannot tell a lie. I left the window open. It rained on our costumes."

"I am George Washington. I cannot tell a lie. I left the window open. It rained on our costumes".

Checking Comprehension and Skills

1. Why do you think the boys and girls in Dan's class warned him to close the window?
2. How do you think Dan felt when the costumes were rained on? (199)
3. Why did Dan write a message on a sign? (200)
4. Do you think Dan's message was a good one? Why or why not? (202)
5. In what way do you think Dan was like George Washington? (195, 202)
●6. Look at the map on page 201. Is the gate closer to the school or to downtown?
●7. Look at the map again. Imagine you are standing where South Street and Second Street meet. Would you be closer to the park or to downtown?

What two words make up the underlined words in the sentences?

○8. At the park, a police captain on <u>horseback</u> saw Dan's sign and stopped.
○9. All the children followed Dan and the captain <u>downtown</u>.

● Graphic Aids: Maps   ○ Structure: Compounds and contractions

The Stars and Stripes

The flag of the United States of America is sometimes called the Stars and Stripes. Each star stands for one of the states in America today. You can find out how many states there were in 1776 by counting the number of stripes on the flag.

Using What You Know

You know many ways the flag is used. You also know many ways to read new words.

Sharpen Your Skills

Here are several ways you've learned to read new words.

- **Sense and consonants** Think of a word you know that makes sense in the sentence. Then see if the consonant sounds in your word are the same as the consonant letters in the new word. What words can fit the next sentence—<u>want</u>, <u>asked</u>, or <u>went</u>?

    We w_nt to see Mount Vernon, where George Washington lived.

- **Vowels** Sometimes you can't be sure of a word just from using the sense and consonants. Either <u>want</u> or <u>went</u> fits the sentence on page 206. The vowel letter will help you.

  We <u>went</u> to see Mount Vernon, where George Washington lived.

- **Compounds and contractions** Compound words are made up of two smaller words you know. Can you read the underlined words?

  George Washington <u>didn't</u> answer the <u>doorbell</u> when we came to his house.

Use one or more of these ways to read the underlined words.

"Old <u>Glory</u>" is another name for the Stars and Stripes. <u>Wouldn't</u> you like to watch Old Glory in the wind? Old Glory is the flag of our <u>homeland</u>.

Use these ways of reading new words as you read "Old Glory."

The Best Day?

Ana buttoned the last button on her Girl Scout shirt. Her mom had cleaned her Girl Scout shirt and pants just for today, the Fourth of July. Ana thought this was the best day of the year—unless she counted the last day of school.

"Now where is my cap?" she said, looking around. She could not carry the flag unless she had on all her Girl Scout clothes.

"Looking for this?" asked her mom holding her cap. "You look great," she said as Ana put her cap on. "Now let's go. Your group is marching fourth in line, so you have to be there soon."

1. What do you think Ana will be doing? Why do you think that?

Ana got to the parade on time. She held the flag proudly as she marched in the parade. The band music was loud, but Ana could hear the flag she held flapping in the wind.

While she marched, Ana thought of what she would do right after the parade. Mom had put the food in the car to take to the park. Had she put in her baseball and bat? Yes, Ana knew she had.

---

2. What do you think Ana will do after the parade? Why do you think that?

The picnic and baseball game lasted the rest of the day. The fireworks would begin soon. The fireworks would light up the night sky. Ana loved watching fireworks. Yes, the Fourth of July was the best day of the year—unless she counted her birthday.

Sharpen Your Skills

As you read, think about what has already happened. Then ask what might happen next.

3. Were your answers to questions 1 and 2 close? If not, how close were your answers?

In the following story, try to figure out what will happen next as you read.

Old Glory

by Carolyn Haywood

The Evans family lives on a farm. One day Mr. Evans made a trip to the hotel in town. He took his children Melissa and Taffy with him in his farm truck. They sat in the truck while Mr. Evans went into the hotel.

On the hotel grounds there was a flagpole with the flag of the United States of America flying from the top. "I like that flagpole," said Taffy. "I wish we had one."

"I do too," said Melissa.

When Mr. Evans climbed back into the truck, Melissa said, "Daddy, I wish we had a flagpole with a flag on top."

"It would be nice," her father said.

"Couldn't we get a flagpole for the Fourth of July, Daddy?" Melissa asked.

"Maybe George Washington would bring us a flagpole," said Taffy.

"George Washington!" Melissa said. "George Washington was the first President of the United States. Right, Daddy?"

"That's right," her father said.

"In school they talked about George Washington," said Taffy. "The Fourth of July is his birthday."

"No, Taffy!" said Melissa. "The Fourth of July isn't George Washington's birthday. His birthday is in the winter. Right, Daddy?"

"Right!" her father said.

"Well, I wish we had a flagpole," said Taffy.

When they got home, Mr. Evans said, "I'll see what I can do about a flagpole."

The children forgot all about the flagpole until one morning when a great long truck turned into the driveway. They saw that the truck was carrying a long, red pole.

When the truck stopped, two men jumped down. "What's that?" Melissa asked.

"It's a flagpole," one of the men said.

"Oh, we want a white flagpole," said Melissa.

"We are going to paint it white," said the man. "Now where's your dad? Go tell him Washington's here with the flagpole."

Melissa and Taffy took off at top speed to look for their father. They found him in the barn. "Daddy! Daddy!" Melissa called. "George Washington is here with the flagpole."

"The flagpole, Daddy!" Taffy called out. "George Washington brought the flagpole!"

Mr. Evans laughed and said, "Well, this will be something for you to watch!"

The children ran back to the truck.

Mrs. Evans came out of the house. "George Washington brought the flagpole, Mom!" said Taffy.

Mrs. Evans read the sign on the truck. Then she said, "It's the Washington Flagpole Company, Taffy, not George Washington."

Mr. Evans said, "We thought this would be a good spot."

"Yes," said the man who seemed to be the boss. "Old Glory will float nicely there."

"Who's Old Glory?" Melissa asked.

"Old Glory!" the boss said again. "Why, Old Glory is the flag of the United States."

"Did you bring Old Glory?" Melissa asked.

"No," the boss said. "We only bring flagpoles. You will have to get the flag."

"Well," said Mr. Evans, "you won't need any help from me. By the way, what are your names?"

"Just call me Lou!" the man said.

"I'm George!" said the boss.

Melissa called to her father, "See!"

Then she and Taffy ran back to the house calling, "Mom, George Washington did bring the flagpole!"

Mrs. Evans laughed, "Well, now we must buy a flag. Then we can have a flag raising."

"What's that?" Taffy asked.

"It will be a picnic on the day we raise the flag for the first time," his mother said. "We will have it on the Fourth of July."

"Who will come to the flag raising?" Taffy asked.

"We will ask all of the neighbors and their children," said Mrs. Evans.

Melissa and Taffy spent the rest of the day watching George and Lou place the flagpole in the ground. At last, the flagpole was up.

"It's up!" Melissa cried, running to the house to find her mother. "The flagpole is up!" Mrs. Evans went with the children to see the flagpole.

Melissa cried, "Oh, they forgot to paint it! They said they would paint it white. But how can anybody get up to the top of the flagpole?"

"They must have a way to do it," her mother said. "You watch."

A while later Melissa called, "Lou's painting the flagpole!"

"He's sitting in a swing painting the flagpole," said Taffy.

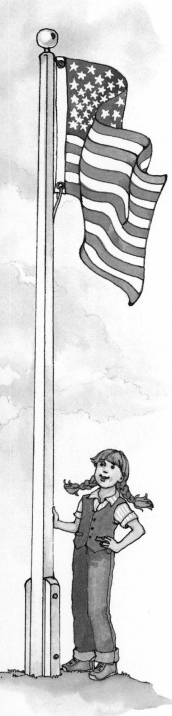

That night Melissa said, "You won't forget to ask everybody to come to the flag raising, will you, Mom?"

"No, indeed!" her mother said. "Everybody will see the flag raising."

"I guess it will be the best Fourth of July that ever was," said Melissa.

Checking Comprehension and Skills

1. Why did Melissa and Taffy think George Washington brought the flagpole? (212, 214)

•2. Melissa thought the men forgot to paint the flagpole. Did you think she was right? Why or why not? (212, 215)

What two words make up the underlined words?

○3. A truck pulled into the driveway.

○4. Now where's your dad?

Which word is best in the blank?

○5. Melissa and Taffy ____ the rest of the day watching George and Lou work.

speed   spent   spill

• Predicting outcomes   ○ Word study strategies

July Fourth

A painting by Grandma Moses

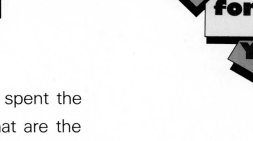

This painting shows how people spent the Fourth of July many years ago. What are the people in the painting doing? Are they doing any of the same things you would do on the Fourth of July?

One Tough Turkey

by Steven Kroll

When the Pilgrims had lived through their first year in the New World, and it was time for the first Thanksgiving, everybody wanted turkey.

But it was hard to catch turkeys. They were all wild in the woods.

"Go and get them!" said the person in charge.

"Right!" said Captain Bill Fitz, chief turkey catcher.

Captain Bill shouldered his musket. He got his best men and his boy Chris. Together they set off for the woods looking for wild turkeys.

There was just one thing they had not counted on. Out in the woods was one tough turkey! His name was Solomon.

As Captain Bill and his men came marching across the field, Solomon watched them. They didn't look very friendly.

Solomon ran back into the woods. He put up a big sign: NO TURKEYS! TURKEYS FLOWN SOUTH FOR THE WINTER!

"What's this?" said Captain Bill.

"It's a big sign," said Chris.

"I know that," said Captain Bill. "What does it mean?"

"It means these turkeys are not telling the truth. Because turkeys don't fly south."

"Then let's go get them!" said Captain Bill. And he waved his musket in the direction of the woods.

Solomon ran and found his wife Regina and his two children, Lavinia and Alfred. He took them to the woods.

"You see those Pilgrims?" Solomon said. "They want us for Thanksgiving dinner. We've got to stop them!"

Lavinia and Alfred strung a rope between the trees. As Captain Bill and his men marched into the woods, they tripped and fell.

While they lay there stunned, Regina put up another sign: PILGRIMS GO HOME!

"What do you think of that?" said Captain Bill.

"They must not like us," said Chris.

"Well, I'll tell you something," said Captain Bill. "We didn't come all the way across the ocean to be treated like this by a flock of turkeys!"

Just then there was a noise behind a tree. "I think we've got one," Captain Bill said softly.

Everybody headed for the tree. Just then they saw a turkey behind a second tree, and then a third.

The Pilgrims didn't know which turkey to chase first.

"Split up into groups, and we will get them all," said Captain Bill.

But no one knew which group to go with, or which group should catch what turkey. They all got so mixed up, they couldn't move.

Solomon was behind the first tree, Regina behind the second, and Alfred and Lavinia behind the third. With the Pilgrims so mixed up, they had lots of time to get away.

At last Captain Bill yelled, "I think they are in those trees."

Solomon looked at Lavinia and Alfred. "You know those bags of old feathers we've been saving? I have an idea."

Solomon gave them his plan. The four of them went to get the big bags of old feathers. They lifted them up into the trees. As the Pilgrims got to the right spot, Solomon, Regina, Alfred, and Lavinia beat on the bags with sticks.

All at once, the Pilgrims were covered in old turkey feathers.

"Surprise!" the four turkeys yelled. Then they raced away into the woods.

"Do you think they'll forget about us now?" Regina asked as they ran.

"I don't know," said Solomon. "You can't ever be sure with these Pilgrims."

Just then Chris jumped out of a tree and landed on Lavinia.

"I got you, turkey!" he yelled.

Lavinia slipped out from under Chris and dashed into the field. Alfred ran after her.

"Look!" yelled Captain Bill. "Turkeys!"

The Pilgrims aimed their muskets. Lavinia and Alfred ducked. There was a loud BANG, but no one was hurt.

Solomon raced out of the woods. He fluffed his feathers and charged at the Pilgrims.

"Father!" said Chris. "Another turkey!"

Captain Bill looked up. "Get him!" he yelled.

Solomon took off across the field. He ran around the trees and out of the woods.

The Pilgrims chased him. But they were not as fast or as clever as Solomon. He led them through many plants that were covered with thorns.

"Yowwwww!" yelled the best men.

"Help!" cried Chris.

"I've had enough of these turkeys!" said Captain Bill. "We are going home!"

Solomon raced to where the other turkeys were hiding. "We fixed them!" he yelled. "Those Pilgrims won't be eating turkey this Thanksgiving!"

Back at home, Captain Bill said what had happened.

"But what about our first Thanksgiving?" everybody asked.

Captain Bill rubbed his brow. "Why not have squash for Thanksgiving?" he asked. "We can just say we had turkey."

And that's just what they did. The Pilgrims ate a lot of squash at the first Thanksgiving. Everybody just thinks they ate turkey.

Books to Read

All Kinds of Families by Norma Simon

What is a family? You will learn about all kinds of families when you read this book.

The Big Balloon Race by Eleanor Coerr

Ariel wants to fly in the big balloon race with her famous mother. Her mother thinks Ariel is too young to fly. Ariel's mother is surprised to find Ariel in the balloon after the race has started.

The Thanksgiving Mystery
by Joan Lowery Nixon

Something in a white sheet has been seen dashing about an apartment building. Susan and Mike find out what it is the day before Thanksgiving.

Glossary

A a

ac·ro·bat a person who can walk on a rope or wire, swing in the air, or do other acts of skill. See the picture.

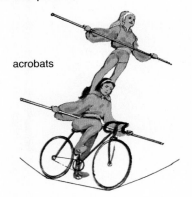

acrobats

a·cross on the other side of: *My house is across the road.*

ac·tor person who acts on the stage, in movies, on TV, or over the radio.

af·fec·tion friendly feeling; love. See the picture.

affection

aim point a gun or direct a blow or throw something at a thing: *He aimed at the tree.* **aimed, aim·ing.**

air what we breathe: *Mountain air is good.*

air·borne in flight: *The plane was airborne by nine in the morning.*

a·maze surprise greatly; strike with wonder: *She was amazed at the magic act.* **a·mazed, a·maz·ing.**

an·swer words spoken after somebody asks a question: *Her answer was ''no.''*

ant a small animal that lives in the ground or in wood. See the picture.

ant

a·part·ment a group of rooms to live in: *There are ten apartments in our building.*

ap·ple·sauce apples cut in pieces and cooked until soft.

arm the part of your body between the shoulder and the hand.

a·ward something given after careful thought; prize: *My dog won the top award.*

B b

bag a container made of paper, cloth, plastic, or leather, that can be closed at the top.

banana|clever

ba·nan·a a fruit that grows in large bunches. See the picture.

banana

bas·ket a container made by dry grass or strips of wood woven together. See the picture.

basket

bees·wax wax made by bees.

boss a person who hires people to work or who watches over and directs them.

breath air taken into and out of the lungs: *Take a deep breath.*

C c

cam·el a large animal that can go a long time without water. See the picture.

cam·er·a a machine for taking pictures or movies.

cap·tain the one who is in charge: *She is captain of the team.*

car·ni·val place of fun having rides, games, and shows.

charge **In charge of** means be at the head of or be the boss of.

child a young boy or girl: *Where is that child?*

chip·munk a small, striped animal like a squirrel. See the picture.

chipmunk

cir·cus a show that goes from place to place. A circus has acrobats and clowns.

class·room room in which classes are held; schoolroom.

clev·er able to do something very well: *She is a clever teacher.* **clev·er·er, clev·er·est.**

camel

230

cliff a steep slope of rock. See the picture.

cliff

climb go up something too steep to walk up: *I climbed a tree.* **climbed, climb·ing.**

close shut: *Close the window.* **closed, clos·ing.** (*Close* rhymes with *rose*.)

cloth what is used to make clothes: *Clothes are made from cloth.*

clothes coverings for a person: *Dresses, pants, and shirts are clothes.*

col·or red, yellow, blue, or any of them mixed together: *I have eight colors in my paint box.*

com·mer·cial a message on radio or TV between or during shows.

com·pa·ny a group of people joined together to run a kind of work or put on a play.

com·plain say that something is wrong: *He complains about the food.* **com·plained, com·plain·ing.**

court·yard a place with walls, in or near a large building.

cous·in the son or daughter of your uncle or aunt.

cov·er anything that protects or hides: *a book cover.*

crown a head covering for a king or queen.

crum·ple crush together: *She crumpled the paper into a ball.* **crum·pled, crum·pling.**

D d

dead with life gone: *Why are the flowers in my kitchen window dead?*

de·part go away: *The train departs at 6:15.* **de·part·ed, de·part·ing.**

dif·fer·ent not the same: *These socks are all different.*

di·rect tell what to do: *Sam will direct the actors in the play.* **di·rect·ed, di·rect·ing.**

doz·en twelve; a group of twelve things; 12.

E e

ear the part of the head by which people and animals hear.

el·bow the part half way down the arm that bends.

elves in a story, tiny beings that are full of tricks. See the picture.

elves

eve·ry·thing every thing; all things: *She did everything she could to help.*

ex·er·cise use over and over: *A dog needs to exercise its body every day.* See the picture. **ex·er·cised, ex·er·cis·ing.**

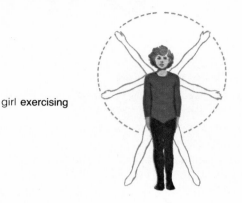

girl **exercising**

ex·tra more than what is needed: *The actors asked for extra pay.*

F f

fa·mous very well known. *The famous singer was greeted by loud clapping.*

fan a machine that stirs the air. See the picture.

fan

fa·vor act of being kind; friendly: *Will you do me a favor?*

feath·er one of the light, thin parts that cover a bird's skin. See the picture.

feather

film take moving pictures or have moving pictures taken for a movie or TV: *They filmed the scene three times.* **filmed, film·ing.**

flag a piece of colored cloth that stands for some country or state or group. See the picture.

the first American **flag**

flash·light a light small enough to carry.

fla·vor taste: *Oranges and apples have different flavors.*

flew See **fly.** *The sea birds flew away.*

flight act or way of flying: *the flight of a bird.*

fly move through the air with wings: *Birds fly.* **flew, flown, fly·ing.**

fourth next after the third; 4th.

front the first part; the part that faces forward: *The front of the house was painted.*

fruit part of a tree, bush, or vine that is good to eat. Apples, oranges, and bananas are fruits.

G g

get be given; come to have: *I hope to get a bike for my birthday.* **got, got** or **got·ten, get·ting.**

glance look quickly: *I only glanced at her.* **glanced, glanc·ing.**

go move along: *Boats go down the river.* **went, gone, go·ing.**

gold·fish a small fish, gold in color, often put in a pool or fish bowl. See the picture.

goldfish

gone See **go**. *She has gone home.*

got·ten See **get**.

grade a class in school: *She is in third grade.*

guess think without really knowing: *I guess it will rain today.* **guessed, guess·ing.**

H h

half one of two parts, each part being the same size: *Half of 6 is 3.*

height how tall a person is; how far up a thing goes: *the height of a mountain. Not many people grow to a height of seven feet.*

he·li·um a very light gas that will not burn, much used in balloons.

ho·tel a building where people can rent rooms to sleep in.

hour one of the 24 parts of one day.

I i

i·de·a a plan, picture, or thought in your head: *Whose idea was it to go to the zoo? We had no idea it was true.*

ID tag identification tag, a tag that gives an animal's name and where the animal lives: *The dog is wearing an ID tag.*

J j

juice the part of fruit or vegetable or meat that flows freely like water.

jun·gle wild land with thick bushes, vines, and trees: *There are jungles in South America.*

K k

king·dom the land ruled by a king or queen.

kiss a touch with the lips as a sign of love.

knee the part half way down the leg that bends.

233

L l

leath·er a strong material made by tanning hides: *Shoes are made of leather.*

lie have your body in a flat way: *I want to lie down.* (Never say, "I want to *lay* down.") **lay, lain, ly·ing.**

M m

mes·sage words or ideas sent from one person to another.

mi·cro·phone a tool for sending sounds. See the picture.

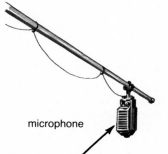

microphone

mod·el a small thing made to look like another: *a ship model.*

mov·ie a moving picture.

Ms. a name put in front of a woman's name.

mus·ket kind of old gun. See the picture.

musket

N n

news·pa·per sheets of paper telling the news.

night the time when it is dark.

O o

oh a word used to show surprise, hurt, and other feelings: *Oh, such wonder! Oh! No!*

op·po·site as different as can be: *North and south are opposite directions.*

or·ange a round, yellow-red fruit, full of juice, that is good to eat. See the picture.

orange

P p

pad soft material used to protect: *Do you have knee pads for the game?*

pair a set of two; two things that go together: *a pair of shoes.*

pa·tience long, hard work: *It takes patience to train wild animals.*

pay give something of worth for things or for work done: *Pay for the dinner.* **paid, pay·ing.**

per·son a man, woman, or child.

pic·nic a meal eaten in the open air.

piece one of the parts of which a thing is made; a bit or scrap: *Put a piece of wood on the fire.*

pi·lot a person who steers a ship, an airplane, or a balloon.

pouch a fold of skin that is like a bag: *Chipmunks have pouches in their cheeks.*

pres·i·dent the person who is head of a country, company, club, or other group.

prob·lem a hard question to be thought about and worked out.

Q q

queen a woman ruler: *The queen rode in the parade.*

R r

raise lift up: *Raise your hand.* **raised, rais·ing.**

re·pair put in good shape again: *Will you repair my torn coat?* **re·paired, re·pair·ing.**

ride sit on something and make it go: *Some people ride camels.* **rode, rid·den, rid·ing.**

rode See **ride.** *I rode my bike to school.*

S s

scen·er·y the painted hangings or screens used on a stage to show when and where the play takes place: *The scenery pictures a shoemaker's shop many years ago.*

scis·sors a tool for cutting, with two sharp blades that move toward each other. See the picture.

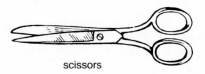

scissors

scout person who is a member of the Boy Scouts or Girl Scouts.

screw·driv·er tool for putting in or taking out screws by turning them. See the picture.

screwdriver

235

sew work on cloth with a needle and thread: *Judy likes to sew.* **sewed, sew·ing.** (*Sew* rhymes with *go.*)

sewing machine

sheet a thin piece of anything: *a sheet of ice, a sheet of paper.*

shoe·mak·er person who makes or mends shoes.

shoul·der the part of your body to which an arm is joined.

shy not at ease in company or with people: *He is shy and doesn't say much.* **shi·er, shi·est.**

south the direction to your right as you face the rising sun.

squash a vegetable that grows on a vine. See the picture.

squash

stage the raised platform where plays are acted: *No one was on the stage.* See the picture.

stage

starve suffer and die with hunger: *Birds starve if we don't feed them in winter.* **starved, starv·ing.**

sto·ry a tale, true or make-believe, of some things that have happened. *I hope he tells us the story of his life.*

stu·dent person who is learning in a school: *That school has 3000 students.*

suit a set of clothes: *My father's new suit has a coat, a pair of pants, and a vest.* See the picture.

suit

switch make different; become different: *The wind switched to the north.* **switched, switch·ing.**

T t

tel·e·phone a tool for talking from one place to another.

tent·mak·er a person who makes tents.

thought have ideas about something. *We thought it would snow today.*

thumb the small, thick finger of the hand.

tough hard to do or know the meaning of: *Math is tough for some students.* **tough·er, tough·est.**

trust think that a person or thing is fair, and true: *I would trust you to get the job done.* **trust·ed, trust·ing.**

truth that which is true: *Tell the truth.*

try·out test made to find out if a person is good at something: *Tryouts for our team will start after school opens.*

tur·key a large bird of America raised for food. See the picture.

turkey

V v

vet·er·i·nar·i·an a doctor who treats animals instead of people. See the picture.

veterinarian

vis·it the act of going to see; coming to see: *Bobby came for a visit.*

W w

warn tell of some danger before it comes: *The police warned us that the road might be under water.* **warned, warn·ing.**

week·end Saturday and Sunday as a time for playing or visiting: *a weekend in the country.*

wheel a round frame that turns on its center.

won got by work or by skill: *This team won the game. We have won the last three games.*

world everybody on earth: *The whole world watched TV to see the ship land.*

wrench a tool to hold and turn nuts. See the picture.

wrench

Y y

yell cry with a strong, loud sound: *He yelled when the door shut on his finger.* **yelled, yell·ing.**

young not old: *Young people like to run.* **young·er, young·est.**

Word List

The words below are listed by unit. Following each word is the page of first appearance of the word.

Unit 1, 11–21

apartment 14
wag 14
tail 14
complain 14
exercise 14
anyone 14
guess 14
loudly 14
goldfish 15
tank 15
anyway 15
story 15
really 16
camel 16
climb 19
lot 20

Unit 2, 22–35

puppies 23
ID tag 26
telephone 27
night 27
kisses 28
friend 28
other 30
newspaper 30
less 31
brush 32
sound 32
roll 33
veterinarian 33

Unit 3, 36–46

classroom 37
wheel 38
can't 38
weekend 40
ant 40
Friday 40
oh 40
scream 40
queen 41
stretch 42
split 42
sand 42
spread 42
yell 42
clothes 42

Unit 4, 47–61

cape 50
basket 50
face 50
zip 50
elves 52
shoemaker 52
cast 52
wife 52
act 52
rise 52
leather 53
pair 53
depart 53
somebody 54
pay 54

cloth 58
fit 58

Unit 5, 62–71

stage 63
ear 65
sew 65
bag 66
scissors 66
crumple 66
piece 66
just 66
hole 67
across 67
thumb 67
sheet 68
front 68
top 68
half 68
scenery 70
luck 70

Unit 6, 72–82

circus 73
answer 74
form 74
tryout 74
clever 76
dead 76
lie 76
didn't 77
burst 78

air 78
popcorn 78
curl 78
acrobat 78
breath 78
idea 78
extra 79
opposite 80
thought 80

Unit 7, 83–95

actor 85
scenes 86
camera 86
direct 86
workers 86
person 86
microphone 87
fruit 89
juice 89
Ms. 89
company 89
I'm 91
film 91
commercial 91
truth 91
orange 91
boxes 93
glasses 93
differently 93
flavor 93
everything 94